About the author

Philip Howard was born in St Helens and [...]
School and Cowley Boys Grammar Scho[...]
10 years before doing a degree as a mature student a[...]
successfully completing a teacher training course he moved to Hull in 1983 to
take up a teaching post at David Lister High School in 1985.

During the three years he spent there he re-established the school's rugby league team which had considerable success in the local area.

In 1988 he transferred to the newly formed Wilberforce Sixth Form College in East Hull. As well as teaching Sociology he was responsible for Special Needs in the college. His duties involved assessing the needs of new students and making sure that they had the necessary support to help them achieve educational success. Under his guidance the college saw a yearly increase in the number of students with a variety of special needs. Students with physical disabilities such as muscular dystrophy, cerebral palsy all achieved educational success in varying degrees. One of his students went on to become the first student with cerebral palsy to obtain a degree at Humberside Polytechnic.

He also found time to qualify as a Level 2 coach and established a rugby league team which saw an increasing number of fixtures develop over the next few seasons. Eventually Wilberforce emerged as National Champions. Due to increasing work commitments the rugby league team was taken over by other members of staff and has continued to enjoy success in recent seasons.

After a successful teaching career he took early retirement in 2009. He is married with three children and nine grandchildren. His main interests are gardening, walking in the Lake District, rugby league and music. He is a member of The Hull male Voice Choir.

Acknowledgements

I would like I would like to thank Steve Morgan for his early encouragement and advice; my wife Linda and my mother for reading and re-reading without ever getting bored or without ever telling me they were; the teachers aides: Caroline, Julie, Mel, Neil, Rene and Sue for lots of laughs amongst the heartache and providing me with so much advice and information; and finally all those young men who were my students who rarely complained and made the best of themselves while they could. I would also like to thank Peter Lush and Dave Farrar of London League Publications Ltd for agreeing to publish the book.
Philip Howard

London League Publications Ltd and Philip Howard would like to thank: Stephen McCarthy for designing the cover and the staff of MPG Biddles Ltd for printing the book.

On page 155, the song is *Another Day*. Music by Delyth Rees, words by Eleri Richards published by Curiad, Pen-Y-Groes, Caernarfon for Hope House, Oswestry.

Muscular Dystrophy

There are several major forms of Muscular Dystrophy which can affect people.

Duchenne (pronounced: due-**shen**) **Muscular Dystrophy (DMD)**, is the most common type of the disease. DMD affects boys. Symptoms usually start between two and six years of age. By age 10 or 12, children with DMD often need to use a wheelchair. The heart may also be affected. They can also develop scoliosis (a curvature of the spine) and tightness in their joints. Over time, all muscles in the body get progressively weaker, and a person might need a ventilator to breathe. People with DMD usually do not survive beyond their late teens or early adulthood.

I do not claim to be an expert on this condition and I have a limited medical knowledge on its causes. During my time as a Special Needs Co-ordinator at Wilberforce Sixth Form College in Hull I met several young men who were affected by this disease. By the time they arrived at college they were already confined to a wheelchair and quite frail. They weren't angels. They were ordinary teenage boys struggling against all odds but what always struck me about each and every one of them was their strength and will to live. They turned up to college every day without complaint and simply got on with it without fuss. I will never forget the stoicism of their parents whose care and devotion were beyond description. I don't know how they managed to keep their lives together. This book is for them.

Many improvements have taken place in our society regarding the issue of disability but there is still much to do. I hope that this story succeeds in showing what huge, positive contributions disabled people can make to society if only we would let them.

For more information, visit the website of the Muscular Dystrophy Campaign, www.muscular-dystrophy.org

Contents

1. Sarah

Sarah was falling. There was a giddy rush in her stomach as she plummeted down into the abyss, into the dark. On and on she fell. Tiny specks of light flickered by at great speed. She tried to grab one of them hoping that it will somehow halt her descent, but to no avail. Deeper and deeper, faster and faster, darker and darker she went. She called out, but no sound emerged.

Suddenly the manner of her fall changed. Now, instead of rushing, she was floating downwards. Her descent was much slower. A gentle, almost beautiful feeling overcame her. The specks of light no longer raced by. She could see them clearly as multi-coloured rings of light that surrounded her. She could almost touch them, but their circumference was always just too wide and out of reach as if the rings knew how far she could stretch. She was floating downwards in a tunnel of light surrounded by darkness.

Still she fell – airless, but without suffocation, and then she landed softly on her back as if placed there by some great hand she could not see. The tunnel of light left and continued upwards without her like some fluorescent jellyfish. She watched it as it moved gradually out of sight, leaving only a pinprick of light in the darkness and stealing any view of her surroundings.

Thinking that her fall had stopped and some sort of safety had been reached, she turned over only to realise that she was perched precariously on a narrow ledge which was part of an invisible cliff face. She understood that a return to where she had come from was impossible. Indeed, she did not know where she had come from. She seemed to have been falling forever, since consciousness began.

Peering over the edge Sarah realised that only the uncertain depths of the abyss awaited her. She was trapped. No mountain rescue will save her from this place. No daredevil helicopter pilot will swing his machine perilously close to the cliff face while her rescuer leaps to bring her back to safety. It was so dark she could not see the cliff face, only sense it. She had a choice. She could stay and face certain death or she could jump. She was wrestling with these options when... she woke up. This was Sarah's dream. Every night it visited her.

Everyone marvelled at her ability to cope with the trials that life had put upon her. No one knew of her inner torment, not even her husband who slept beside her, not even her mother.

What would be the point of telling them?

What could anyone do to change things?

Sarah was travelling on a path that could not be changed. It was a path that was full of pain. She knew what to expect and had prepared herself. She also knew that she must not yield. Others depended on her. She could not give in and she could not, must not, run away. Every day she faced her challenge without complaint and with a smile, but every night she returned to bed to face sleep that would provide no rest.

Sarah was now 34. Her dream was over a year old. It had crept silently into her unconscious. She couldn't remember when or how it arrived. It just had. It had become something she lived with as a matter of course. It no longer frightened her as it first had when she did not understand its meaning. Now she understood it well. She was used to it, and although familiarity had not bred contempt she knew it was not her friend. She simply accepted its existence as a fact of life as she did the beads of sweat that trickled down her forehead in the early hours of the morning. As daylight replaced darkness Sarah lay there, damp, watching the ceiling.

She had spent the first 13 years of her life in the coalmining town of Hamilton in Scotland. Just before her 14th birthday her family dragged her unwillingly from a place she loved and moved south to another mining town. Castleton was just inside Yorkshire's border with Lancashire in the north of England. As a result her accent developed a particular lilt to it, a mixture of Lanarkshire, Lancashire and Yorkshire.

They had moved to the Yorkshire coalfields because her father had got a job as a senior engineer at Preston Manor colliery. It had been a significant opportunity and her family saw a considerable improvement in its finances. Sarah had not appreciated this. Such a move is always difficult for a teenager, facing the trauma of separation from her childhood friends. Her parents' view that she would soon make new friends proved more difficult than first thought.

Not only did she have a different accent, but she also had red hair. She was doubly different and children can be very cruel. However, Sarah had managed to survive. She had a strong character and sharp nails. She was able to fend off every bully she came up against. People crossed her at their peril. Gradually she earned respect and made one or two friends at school although her main friends were her family. Sarah grew up strong and fiercely loyal.

The pit had strong ties with a local amateur rugby league team, Preston Manor Miners. Although the team still had many miners in its ranks, it was no longer made up entirely of miners. Indeed as it developed youth teams, it took boys in from all walks of life.

By the time she was 16, Sarah's brothers, Tom and James, were both playing for the club's first team. Tom had even been selected for the Yorkshire county team despite his Scottish birth and it was hoped that his younger brother would also receive a similar honour in the near future. Sarah had stood on many a winter's Saturday afternoon screaming as a match progressed. She had loved it and her shouts and screams were well recognised. Retired prop forwards who stood over six foot two and weighed around 17 stones shied away from this red haired waif who produced power in her voice that came from uncharted depths.

Sarah couldn't help herself. She always became thoroughly involved in the games and the fact that her brothers were playing stirred her passions further. She was part of their team, felt every knock and revelled in every victory. As the young sister she would tag along with her big brothers, she was their biggest fan.

Rugby league was an important part of community life. It produced a strong sense of community spirit and the team was well supported by both men and women, although it was to be a few years before girls would take an active part on the pitch as they do now.

When she was 17 she had begun to notice one of her brothers' team mates who had joined from another club that season. David Burgess was a tall, strong second-row forward with powerful thighs and beautiful curly blonde hair. He didn't look rough enough to play this game until he stepped out onto the pitch, when he changed completely. He was certainly rough alright, but she had liked that; the contrast between gentleness and raw brute power. The first time that he spoke to her she was touched by his gentle shyness. She found this character mix intriguing. He fitted the term 'gentle giant', to a tee. She had seen him take and give severe physical punishment in a county final, only to sweep his young nephew up in his arms in celebration at the final whistle.

Sarah watched his progress with interest. At the end of a match she would congratulate or commiserate with her brothers, but she always tried to direct a word or two in his direction. He would smile or grunt depending on the result. He didn't like losing; that was clear. Despite her earnest attempts to speak to him, David hardly seemed to notice her. It didn't occur to her that perhaps her timing was poor, that after 80 minutes of unrelenting physical effort, the young man might not be in a position to show any interest in her.

He had been at the club a whole year and despite her attempts to be noticed, they had barely spoken to each other, so she had been completely taken aback when he asked her if he could walk her home after the club's Christmas party. She managed to conceal her excitement and accepted nonchalantly. They had walked back to her home along deserted streets covered by a light fall of snow, the first and only, as it turned out, fall of that year. Normally, Pennine areas get greater amounts of snow than other parts of England because of their northern location and height above sea level.

As they walked, they instinctively leant into each other as protection against the cold. He put his arm around her and she tucked herself further into his coat. The conversation never faltered, not even on that first uncertain night. She had never forgotten that walk home; the unblemished snow on the footpath, the stillness as people stayed warm indoors and the view, down the slight gradient, of street lights bouncing light off snowflakes.

They stood at her parent's front door holding each other without speaking. As she looked up at him a snowflake landed on her nose. He wiped it off gently, but his woollen gloves merely left traces of more snow on her cheek. They grinned at each other as she wiped it away herself. Then they stopped grinning and looked at each other in silence. His goodnight kiss was soft and warm. Sarah had almost laughed as he bent down to kiss her, but she didn't. She didn't want him to think anything was wrong.

Sarah smiled at his back as he gingerly negotiated his way down the narrow path, his broad shoulders knocking snow off the privet hedge as he went. As he turned and closed the gate he waved with a gentle, almost inaudible "Bye. You go in now." He made sure that she had opened the door and was safely inside before leaving.

Sarah watched from the warmth of her hallway until her father's cry of "Shut the bloody door. It's freezing!" pushed her onto the step once more. She turned to pull the door to and made certain that it did not shut on her. She looked up again in his direction, only to find that he had disappeared from view. Sarah stood there watching an empty space. She knew then that she was going to marry him.

Three months later he proposed to her on top of Alma's Crag which stood one mile to the west of town. They had set off for a walk on Sunday morning at 11 o' clock. It was a beautiful crisp March morning.

Alma's Crag is a hill with a rocky top that can be seen from anywhere in town. Walkers follow the road before turning right through a farmer's gate. From there a cart track skirts a stone wall before it leaves the wall and passes through woodland. The track becomes a footpath and suddenly begins to steepen. It then opens onto grassland revealing a clump of rocks resting at the summit like walkers weary from their exertions

They had reached the top by 12.15pm. The sun had remained and the crisp spring morning had transformed into a pleasant afternoon that was warm for the time of year. There was a soft, grassed dip in the middle of an outcrop of rock. Running the last 50 yards, she whooped as they dropped into it in one movement. Breathless she wrapped her arms around him and they embraced.

They kissed warmly and then looked at each other. Without speaking, they nestled deeper into their private world, the silence disturbed only by the sounds of their rising passion.

They lay there in silence, nestled against one another, hidden and protected, alone, together. Sarah couldn't remember if she had drifted into a brief sleep, using his arms as a pillow. After a while he lifted his head and she seemed to wake up. She could see the seriousness in his eyes as he looked directly into hers.

"I love you".

"I love you too".

"Will you marry me?"

"Yes. You know I will."

Then they cuddled once more, silent, lost in each other, totally in love. It was perfect; a perfect day and a perfect love. As they got up, however, an observant eye would have noticed the formation of clouds on the horizon. What no one could foresee was the dark storm clouds behind, still nascent and immature, but growing and threatening and heading straight for them.

She was not surprised that he had asked her after such a short time. It had seemed the most natural thing to do. People thought she was pregnant. Her mum and dad had been shocked, but they had not tried to stop it. They could hardly talk, having got married within a year of meeting each other themselves. Perhaps it was genetic!

Five months later they were married, at 2.15pm in St Ann's Church on the edge of town. The weather was glorious, with not a cloud in the sky. It was a beautiful August day. It had all been perfect, so very, very, perfect. She could not have been happier. He was 23 and she was 19.

By the time she was 20 she was pregnant. Over the next few years, life progressed well. They hardly ever rowed despite the strain of two children under five years of age. Melanie had been followed two years later by Karl and finally James. He had been an accident. They had decided that they could afford two kids, but passion had interfered with finance and he had been born two months before Karl's fourth birthday. They never had any money, but people made comments about how happy they were and what nice kids they had.

Home was a plain council house built in the 1950s. They could have had a miner's house, rented from the then National Coal Board, but decided against it on the grounds that they would have had to move out if Dave ever left mining.

"We were poor, but we were happy" seemed a terrible cliché but it was true. They led simple, uncomplicated lives.

It was not to last.

2. Diagnosis

Karl was four before his parents realised that there was a problem. Looking back, the signs had been there even earlier. He had been slow to start walking, but they had not thought too much about it. The odd person had made comments, but it didn't seem to be too much to worry about.

"He'll walk when he's ready. He's as bright as a button. I'm sure there's nothing to worry about," her father had said on more than one occasion, but Sarah's doubts lingered.

Then they had noticed that there was something unusual in the way he walked. He seemed to waddle and be unsteady on his feet.

"Perhaps he needs arch supports." Dave's mother had said. "Our Dave needed them when he was little to help straighten his feet out. He walked with his feet turned inwards and he kept falling just like Karl does." Sarah decided to take him to the doctors, but then he seemed to improve and reassured she didn't pursue it.

"I think I've been worrying too much," she said to Dave.

"Well that's a mother's job," he replied. He held her in his arms and she felt safe as she always did when he wrapped his arms around her.

She stopped worrying for a while, but when he fell over at a friend's party, she realised that something had to be done. Without warning Karl had crumpled to the ground as if he had no strength whatsoever in his legs. He looked up in shock, unable to move and children around him laughed. Sarah and Dave ran to him, picked him up and comforted him. Sarah saw her concern mirrored in her husband's face and without speaking they agreed that their son needed to be looked at. Things were clearly not right and her dad's reassurances no longer worked.

Karl sat in his mother's arms unwilling to move from her. Sarah hated to see him like that, but stayed because she feared that leaving the party that he had so looked forward to would upset him further. She needed no second chance when he said that he wanted to go home. He was asleep before they got out of the door, the events having clearly exhausted him.

"We'll take him to the doctor's tomorrow. I'm not due on until the afternoon. Everything will work out fine love. Don't worry. They'll sort it out."

Sarah nodded, but said nothing. She did not believe her husband's reassuring comments. If her son's sleeping head had not obscured the expression on Dave's face she would have seen that he did not believe them either.

Their GP, Doctor Fitzpatrick, was in his late 20s. He looked like he was trying to combine being a professional with being young and cool.

He was dressed in a white shirt and red waistcoat with black trousers. He smiled, and shook hands before inviting them to sit down.

Sarah described Karl's symptoms to him and mentioned that her husband had needed supports for his feet when he was a child.

"Well let's have a look at him then." He asked Karl to walk to his mummy, but he was shy and unwilling so Sarah walked with him. As she looked at Karl she did not notice the doctor's eyes move away from his feet to observe the alignment of his legs. She did not see the doctor's expression change from concentration into concern.

"Okay, that's all I need to see for now." Sarah and Dave watched the doctor stare at their son. He did not speak. After a few seconds he took a deep breath and said, "Would you excuse me for a minute. I'd like Doctor Jennings to have a look at Karl."

"Why what's wrong?" Suddenly Dave's calm assurance of the previous day had disappeared.

"I just want some assistance. I won't be a moment." He left the room and returned moments later with an older doctor, grey haired and dressed in a corduroy jacket. He looked like a man of experience, a man who knew what he was on about.

Again Karl performed for the doctors. This time both Sarah and Dave saw them exchange knowing glances. They both stood up simultaneously.

"Would you excuse us?" Before they could say yes or no the doctors were outside in a discussion. A moment later Doctor Fitzpatrick returned. He sat down and looked at both of them in turn. He no longer seemed to be quite as young and trendy as he had when they first walked in. He told them that he thought Karl had a serious problem and that he would refer him immediately to a specialist. The doctor then told them not to panic.

Sarah and Dave looked at each other. What do you do when a doctor tells you not to panic? You panic.

"Doctors make things better don't they? That's what they are there for. They don't tell you not to panic." Sarah could hear the panic in her own voice and she could feel it growing deep inside her.

"It's okay love. He's just being cautious." Sarah searched her husband's face for crumbs of comfort, but found none. He couldn't sort this one out and if he was lost, so was she. The feeling of panic increased when they got an appointment within a fortnight. That morning Sarah had woken up as normal at 5am. Despite the fact that he always insisted that he was okay, she always got up to make sure Dave had time to eat a proper breakfast. She had a very traditional view of the role of a full-time mother and housewife. She waved him off to work at 5.40am and returned to bed for a sleep before the kids woke up.

At 7am she got up as usual, woken by the sound of the children's chatter. After breakfast Sarah put them in front of the television to keep them entertained while she washed the breakfast dishes and tidied the table.

She heard the creaking gate that signified the arrival of the postman. Every day she opened the door to greet him. As he thrust a bundle of paper into her hand she looked at the mail and noticed the hospital's name immediately. Shutting the door, she realised that she had forgotten to say thank you and turned, but the gate had creaked shut. She stared at the empty space transfixed and then her eyes returned to the handful of mail. In her hand lay the usual junk, an unrequested catalogue, and a magazine for tools that Dave had once ordered something from years ago. She let them drop to the floor while keeping hold of the white envelope.

Her hands shook as she tore at it. She stopped and looked at it, without reading. Clutching the letter in both hands as if it were a valuable object, she walked into the kitchen and sat down at the table. She was dimly aware of children's laughter as they enjoyed the cartoon on television. She stared at it and did not move. The appointment was in three weeks time.

"That's quick," she thought. A look at the calendar on the wall showed that it was precisely 13 days since they had been to her GP.

Thirteen days is not a long time to wait for a hospital appointment, but it is an age to keep panicking. Three more weeks. Maybe the speed was a good thing. Dave was right to be positive. Maybe they would deal with it quickly before things got serious.

"Serious?" Why had she thought of that word?

She looked at the calendar once more, as if to check that the dates hadn't changed, and then back at the letter. Three weeks. Suddenly the significance of the speed of events struck her.

"Don't panic."

"Panic?" There was so much in one word. Something was seriously wrong with their son.

They arrived at Castleton Hospital at 2.22pm. She remembered the time exactly. Something inside her was focussing her every move, preparing for something she didn't want to face, but from which there was no escape.

When people experience such a day as they did the details burn into their very souls. They do not forget the day that they are told that their little boy is going to die, slowly and painfully and in front of them and that they will be unable to do anything to save him.

Wet autumn leaves had mashed together to line the side of the driveways. Bare trees waived in the cold windy sky. It was one of those days when it didn't know whether to rain or shine. One minute it was bright, then it was dark and at 3.10pm precisely it had got very dark indeed.

Having parked at the front of the hospital they had walked with Karl round to the out patients department. As they approached the clinic door a porter came through from the other side. Smiling, he held the door as they pushed the buggy through. Pausing between the outer and inner doors to shake the rain from their clothes and gather themselves they looked at each other.

They stood in that confined protected space as if in a time capsule. For a moment they seemed protected, as if what they feared was about to happen could be avoided. They stood face-to-face looking into each other's eyes. Dave touched Sarah's cheek and smiled softly.

"I love you."

"I love you," she said. In silence she looked at him. He so wanted to make it safe, to protect her, them both. Then a nurse busily, unaware of their fears, came through the outer door, carrying some files and broke the capsule's seal.

"Excuse me please." She danced round them both, smiled and walked on through the inner doors and down the corridor. The spell was broken, the illusion of safety shattered. They stood there, fearful and vulnerable.

"Are you ready?"

"No. Are you?"

"No" he said tenderly. They pushed open the second doors and entered the reception area. Sarah handed over the appointment letter to the clerk who completed all the registration details. This was about their son and although she knew he would receive all the care and attention he needed, she knew that here he was just another name on a list among lots of lists.

They sat in the waiting room. Karl sat on his father's knee and listened as he read a story to him from a selection on the table. *Days of Frog and Toad* was a series of short stories in which Toad helped Frog to deal with difficulties. As he sat there reading, Dave silently wished that someone could sort out theirs.

They had been so happy, but as she and Dave sat there they became silent, absorbing the fact that all the other kids in the waiting room were either in wheelchairs or callipers (aides to help them walk).

Suddenly their unspoken fears began to crystallise as they realised that they were in deep trouble. When the nurse came out and shouted Karl's name, Dave instinctively reached for Sarah's hand as they carried their child down the yellow walled corridor covered in pictures of children's television characters and official notices. Still they didn't speak to one another. They didn't need to.

9

An hour later they were returning down the same bright corridor. Dave coughed, trying not to cry. Sarah felt no such inhibition. Everyone had been so kind. No one could have done more. They had watched Karl being examined by a team of medical experts. Strangers had moved his limbs in their hands and asked him to walk when he wanted to stay with his mummy. He had cried and screamed. They had all been so gentle, so kind. They, the consultant, Mr Abrahams, two registrars and another junior doctor whose names they never registered had explained their findings to them. Karl had muscular dystrophy.

They had heard of it, but had never known what it was or even cared to know. Now they were finding out in unbearable detail. The doctors rattled off their knowledge. Besides the unusual pattern of walking and the tendency to fall over, which had made them see their doctor in the first place, they told them that the muscular dystrophies were a group of muscle diseases which had three features in common: they were hereditary; they were progressive; and each caused a characteristic, selective pattern of weakness.

It was like having a medical textbook read off about your little boy. Each word slammed into them as if they were being stoned to death by some barbaric executioners.

They were told that Muscular Duchenne Dystrophy had no cure. As he got older Karl's muscles would become weaker and as his heart was a muscle, that too would waste. While the effects of the disability could be slowed by physiotherapy, its progress could not be stopped. By the time he reached nine he would need a wheelchair and by his teenage years he would be almost totally dependent on others, unable to feed or toilet himself. He would do well to survive into his 20s.

They were told a great deal of information much of which rushed past them in a flood that would take weeks and months to understand let alone come to terms with.

They had nodded when they were asked if they were all right, but it was an automatic response. Of course they weren't. They even thanked the people who had just outlined the terrible future for their son.

They were given a cup of tea and allowed to absorb the shock, but Karl was becoming restless so they decided to leave. They walked along the yellow corridor past yet more children in callipers and wheelchairs. Someone opened a door for them and they smiled a smile they didn't want to give.

Dave's hand slipped into hers as they walked, zombie like, towards the car. Their son was going to die. His disability, the word banged into them, disability, was going to get worse and worse and as they tried to escape the smothering confines of the building it was clear that there was no escape.

10

This happened to others, not to them. They were happy, they had everything to live for and to look forward to. This couldn't be happening to them. Before they knew it they were back at the car. Anger and fear hit them both in equal amounts. Dave started the engine and she placed her hand on his.

"No, not yet. I just want to stay here just for a minute." Dave nodded and switched off the engine. They sat there recalling the doctor's words repeated once more: "By the time your son is nine or 10, he will need a wheelchair on occasion, by 12 or 13 he will be confined to one. I'm sorry, but there is no cure."

"No cure?"

"No cure."

They sat there for several minutes, listening to the rain as they had often done before they were married. Then it had cocooned them. The car had been the lovers' only place of privacy and driving rain often sealed them in. Now it seemed to smother them.

Fortunately, Karl had fallen asleep immediately. The last hour had been exhausting for him.

"I don't understand." said Sarah.

"What? What don't you understand?" shouted Dave.

"How it could happen. There's no one else in our family. I don't understand." The rain muffled her fading voice. Dave snorted dismissively. It didn't matter that there was no history in the family. The fact was that it was there now and they were faced with it. Dealing with it was another matter. So much had been said in the consultant's room. Advice, explanations, sources of help, but all that would take time. What confronted them now was the awful, crushing feeling that life had stopped, that the rain was the monster beating at the door, trying to get in and devour them.

They sat there, timeless, silent. Through the hedge that formed the boundary of the car park, they could see car lights flash by. The world had not stopped. Lots of different worlds in motor cars carried on as if nothing had happened. Separate lives lived in their own little boxes with their own troubles, knowing nothing of each other's. He was asking himself 'Why didn't these other people know about their tragedy? How could they simply pass on by without casting even a blink in their direction?' And that made him think, 'How many other tragedies were happening right now? What right had he to expect others to know about his? Had he ever thought about anyone else's? When you shout at someone who makes a silly mistake in a car, what agonies are they dealing with only to be confronted by some uncaring idiot with a horn and a temper?'   Thoughts flashed to and fro in his mind as life passed on outside. They were going to have to deal with this by themselves. Sarah turned to Dave, her love and her companion. He was gripping the steering wheel as if he was about to collide with a brick wall. Tears were streaming silently down his face. Her rock on so many occasions was crumbling before her as his little boy, his football companion, his wrestling opponent...

Holding back her tears she leaned across, stroked his temple with the back of her hand and whispered "I love you".

Dave nodded and grunted weakly.

"We are going to deal with this aren't we?" Dave nodded again as the tears continued and then he broke into uncontrollable sobs. She pulled her lover to her and they sat there in the car consumed by the rain.

In the back a little four year old child, unaware of his parents' pain, began to snore and dreamed a four year old's dreams oblivious to the trials that lay in front of him.

3.   Life goes on

At first, Sarah and Dave were in desperate emotional state when Karl's illness was diagnosed. To their surprise however, nothing radical happened and Karl continued to grow just like any other child. There were some differences. He walked differently, moving on the forward part of his foot with the heels off the ground. He appeared clumsy to others who were unaware of his situation, but in reality these appeared as minor issues.

What was really different, however, was his mother and father's attitude to life. They had decided, unconsciously at first, that they and he would enjoy the time that they had. In a strange way, the illness became a blessing. They took nothing for granted and began to see positives in almost everything. Every achievement by Karl and the other children was celebrated and rewarded.

Karl's first day at school, Melanie's first 25 metres swim, and James's first steps on his own. All these things that other families enjoyed were enjoyed more.

Once they talked about it. They talked about how important it was to support each other. They decided that they would do their best to minimise pointless rows and recognise them for what they were, a sign of stress. Sarah tried to be brave and put a positive slant on the conversation. She tried to say how Karl's illness had brought them closer together.

"It's something I could have done without" was the terse reply and they never openly discussed it again. Sarah knew she didn't believe what she had said, but what else was there to say? They couldn't go about crying, "Woe is me" all the time, but at the same time they had to deal with reality. She wanted to be happy even if she wasn't. It was a survival technique. She was not going to let the situation grind her, and them, down. Karl needed them. So they didn't talk, they didn't analyse. They simply got on with it. They developed a routine to deal with life just like other families dealt with theirs.

Of course, it wasn't quite that simple. They did have a cloud over them. It was a dark, menacing cloud that constantly threatened stormy weather and it rumbled on continuously. Perhaps not talking about it was for the best, but it also had its dangers. How and when would they tell Karl? What about Melanie and James? They had a right to know, but how much should they know? Telling them would upset them. Not telling them might upset them more if they found out by accident. They felt as if they were between a rock and a very hard place and so, for the time being, they said nothing.

In the absence of any better ideas, they carried on. Dave continued working at Preston Manor colliery as a fitter and Sarah continued as a full-time mum.

Over time the condition became more obvious. Karl's walking difficulties became more pronounced and they made regular visits to hospital for check ups. His joints became increasingly restricted in their movement. First it was the ankles, and then later, it could be seen in his knees. The doctors advised physiotherapy, not to stop this process, but to slow it down and try to maintain Karl's quality of life for as long as possible. They explained that in the future, his hips and his upper body would be similarly restricted and he would need a wheelchair. They couldn't say when, but normally it was about 14 or so.

Things changed gradually. Social services became involved. Little things like grab rails in the bathroom were installed. Then, two days after his eighth birthday, they received a letter from the school. It explained the increasing difficulties at school and informed them that a meeting had been called to discuss Karl's future education and care.

They entered the headmaster's office. Alan Sutton was a kindly looking man in his late 50s. He wore a grey suit with matching beard. He bade them to sit down.

"I wanted to speak to you in private before the meeting begins," he explained. "We want to talk to you about what happens next. The people who are coming to this meeting are very experienced at dealing with children with special needs. They know more than I do. We see several students every year who require extra help, but we only occasionally see someone who has as many difficulties as Karl. These people are the experts. What I want you to understand is that it is the policy of the education authority to keep children in as normal an environment as possible. That is only right and proper. I want to assure you that we will do everything in our power to keep Karl at this school for as long as is possible."

He paused to let the effects of his words sink in. He wanted to see what their reaction would be to the possibility of their child being transferred to a special school. Often these meetings could be quite emotional. Some parents could become angry. They felt that the school was failing their child. He wanted to give them time to realise what was happening, but he saw no reaction. They sat there, both of them, simply listening. They were in his hands. They seemed resigned and trustful; believing that what was about to happen was for the best. He watched them blink in unison, waiting for his next words.

"Do you understand what I am saying?"

Mr Burgess bowed his head. Mrs Burgess coughed and spoke softly.

"How long?"

"Before?"

"Before he has to go to a special school?"

The headmaster sighed. Thankfully they knew the situation.

He spoke as gently and directly as he could: "I don't know. That's what these people will decide. They will tell us but we want to, I want to assure you that everything will be done to ensure that it is done in a way that ensures that Karl is as happy as possible." They nodded in silence. They simply stared at him. He wanted to do something to help them but there wasn't anything to do.

"Would you like a cup of tea?"

Mrs Burgess coughed again, "No thank you".

"Mr Sutton?"

"Yes?"

"Could we just get this over with as soon as possible?" Sarah looked at her husband. She knew how he hated these meetings. He half turned his head to her and gave her a pained smile.

"Of course. I just wanted to be sure you understand what is happening."

"I understand."

A tear rolled down her cheek. Mr Burgess rolled uncomfortably in his seat. He took his wife's hand but said nothing. His head remained bowed.

She coughed once more and spoke almost in a whisper. "I understand that my son is going to die and there's nothing I can do. I know what will happen. I'm not so sure that I'm bothered about the details right now so if it's all the same. I'd rather get this over with."

There was a pause.

"If you don't mind."

"Of course," Mr Sutton whispered in return and tried to think of what to say next. Fortunately his intercom buzzed and broke the silence. His secretary informed him that everyone had arrived.

"Are we ready?" relieved that the awkwardness had been removed.

"Yes." They stood up. Dave and Sarah hugged each other and patted each other gently on the back. Alan Sutton suspected that they had done quite a lot of that over the last few years. He gave them a moment as they gathered themselves together and then he showed them into the conference room.

The meeting took 30 minutes. Sutton had known them to take an hour longer. He had had a word with the head teacher of the special school and together they steered the meeting through. It was agreed that Karl would transfer to Albert Williams School at the beginning of the next academic year. It was agreed that mum and dad would tell him what was going to happen, but that before this he would go on a trip to visit the school. It was agreed that if he saw the school first before he was told that it was to be his new school, he might have a more positive outlook on moving there if he'd already seen how nice it was.

15

Alan Sutton escorted them to their car. They shook hands and he watched them drive off. He sighed. "How do you deal with a situation like that?" He shook his head slowly as he turned towards his office to prepare the agenda for the next governors' meeting.

So in April they went round the school. Its layout and design catered for disabled people. All buildings were single storey. Doorways were wide and electrically operated. They saw lessons in operation that were properly staffed. One teacher might have to teach about 10 children and had teacher's aides as support. There was a clear emphasis on achievement and disability was minimised. The emphasis was on what kids could do rather than what they couldn't do. Everywhere they could see displays of children's artwork and writing.

The parents were very impressed. The question was, was Karl? They had agreed to let the visit sink in and then they would broach the subject a couple of days later but as they were driving home, Karl said, "Is that my new school?"

"What makes you think that dear?"

"One of the kids asked me was I coming to them next year?"

"Would you like to?"

"Dunno."

"Will I be there till I die?"

There was a stunned silence.

"Who said you were going to die?"

"Shit." Dave whispered audibly as he pulled the car into a lay-by and switched off the engine.

"I am going to die aren't I?" Sarah felt sick, but her son needed an answer. "Nobody knows yet. They may find a cure," blurted out Dave.

Sarah looked at Dave in horror. Did he really believe that? She hoped not. If he did then she had not realised how badly her husband was dealing with the situation they were in. Her big strong, rugby league playing husband was not dealing with his son's illness. She put her hand on his as he gripped the wheel. She could feel his anguish.

"Karl. You have got a nasty illness. No one knows what will happen but it isn't good."

"So I'm going to die then?" While Sarah struggled to answer, Karl leant forward and touched his mother's shoulder. He spoke very softly and said, "Don't worry, I'll be okay. Honestly, I will."

He looked at her so earnestly she couldn't speak. She simply smiled. "Shall we go home? I'm dying for a cup of tea aren't you?" He smiled and with that simple resolution, they drove home.

They put Karl to bed and then got Melanie and James ready as normal, each one knowing that the other was desperate to talk.

"Are you all right mummy?" asked Melanie as Sarah tucked her into bed. "Yes love. Why?"

"Cos you and dad seem upset. Have you been rowing?" Sarah smiled at this grown up question. "No, daddy and I are tired that's all."

The conversation with Karl had been brief but traumatic and yet a strange thing had happened. Part of the cloud hanging other them lifted. Much of it remained and would do so forever, but enough lifted to allow a little sunlight in. For a while they could all relax.

Sarah did have to pursue one thing though. Did Dave really believe that a cure might be found? It was not only important for Karl but for Dave's mental health. Hopes were important, delusions were dangerous. So two days later, when the kids had gone to bed, she asked him.

He said no, of course he didn't believe it. He had simply been at a loss to know what to say.

"Are you sure?"

He nodded, his head bowed, as it had been in the headmaster's study, unable to look at her. For a long time they sat there in silence. Then he said "We don't deserve this."

"Nobody deserves this. This is the hand we've been dealt and there's nothing we can do except make sure that we and Karl are as happy as possible. It's our duty to be happy."

They held each other for an age, both unwilling to be the one who made the separation. As she spoke, Sarah was able to look at them both from outside herself. She listened to what she was saying and it was obvious that they both were going to look after their son, but she was also going to have to look after her husband.

Karl didn't mention it to the others but both of them knew that they would have to broach the subject soon. They wanted to control the way in which their other children found out. The first thing was to get Karl settled into his new school.

Karl started at Albert Williams School in September. Despite their initial fears, the first day passed off remarkably well. Karl was delighted to be going to school in a special bus that came and picked him up. A large, white bus with the words Education Department on the side pulled up outside at 8am precisely. They had suggested that Sarah go with him on the first day so that he could get used to the transport and the new people. Karl had told her in no uncertain terms that she didn't need to bother. He could manage. He was a big boy now.

Sarah realised that she had to let him get on with it. She was pleased how easily Karl was adapting to his new lifestyle and she prayed that it wasn't a show just for her sake, that he wasn't suffering a deep trauma inside. If it was a show it was a very good one. He greeted Sue, the escort on the bus, as if they were old friends instead of someone he'd met just the day before as part of his induction.

He walked out in his callipers and sat in the wheelchair that she had brought from the bus. She took him to the rear where Tony, the driver was waiting with the bus's tailgate lowered. As it rose with him on it Karl turned and waved to his mum. He was actually enjoying himself, perched like royalty above the common herd. He waved to neighbours and seemed delighted that they waved back. Karl was being noticed. In his eyes, he was somebody important. Tony shut the rear door as Sue made certain that Karl was secure. Sarah stood there with her hand still raised after the bus had gone.

"He'll be fine. He's a tough lad." The voice belonged to Rene, her elderly neighbour.

"Yes. He's a tough lad." She smiled at her and against her better judgement said, "Would you like a cup of tea?"

There was nothing wrong with Rene. She was a nice old dear but once you got her in your house it was impossible to get rid of her. If the truth were known, however, Sarah did not feel like doing any housework. Rene came round the privet hedge that separated their house at 8.25am. She left at noon. It didn't matter. It meant that four o' clock wouldn't be too far away.

Karl settled in very quickly at school. Everyone was very pleased with him. He made lots of new friends as children do. He was sad that only Robert remained in touch from the old school. They had been friends since they were three. Life continued as normal. Melanie, his elder sister, knew what the situation was. They had decided to tell her early on. The imminent arrival of a special bus was not something they would be able to cover up. She responded very positively. She just got on with it and played the role of helpful big sister. They, that is, mum, dad, Karl and Melanie all agreed not to tell James for the time being, until he was older and to their credit, the two children never risked upsetting their little brother.

Somehow they managed to live as normal a life as possible. Of course it wasn't normal. Very few children from Castleton get to go to Disneyland. The money was raised by people in their street who had been fantastic. As more and more people heard about Karl they came out of the woodwork to help raise funds.

Not every nine year old meets their favourite television personality. He spent a full day at Granada studios with him. He was hilarious and parents and children alike had had a great day. A signed picture of Karl with his hero now hung on his bedroom wall next to a photograph of Chris Anderton, a local rugby league star who was Karl's favourite player.

It was a normal life. Sarah made certain it was. She made a point of seeing the positive wherever possible. She kept an eye on everything and everyone. She refused to allow self pity to enter any conversations. Her parents kept saying how strong she was. Her in-laws fussed over them all and Ma, Dave's mum used to have a quiet word in the kitchen, "just to check if everything was okay." Sarah always told them that things were fine and Ma too would say how well she was coping and how strong she was. They did not know that Sarah had a secret. She was not as strong as she appeared.

Every night, ever since Karl had started special school, she had been having the same dream. She couldn't say why it had started when it did. Perhaps Karl's start at the new school had brought everything into a sharper focus, forcing her to face the reality that she had known existed, but had not dealt with. Perhaps this change had told her that she could not stop what was going to happen and that it was getting closer. The world that she and Dave had known had gone forever. Sarah was trapped in a situation beyond her control.

This was her ledge. There was no way up or down. All she could do was wait and make the best of things. Sarah might have looked strong but like the figure on the ledge she felt scared, vulnerable and most of all guilty. It was her fault, wasn't it? She had given birth to him. The dream was her punishment.

4. Dave

Each night she found herself falling, only to land on the same ledge. The dreams were so regular and the detail so repetitive that it had become her ledge. She owned it, but that did not put her in charge. She was trapped between the cliff and the abyss, surrounded in silence, smothered by darkness.

Every morning she awoke and gasped. At first she thought that her bed is the ledge and found herself clutching the sheets for support. Then slowly the light of dawn would filter through the lace curtains. She would hear the familiar ticking of the clock and realise that she had landed in the safety of her bedroom. She would turn to her bedside cabinet and take a sip of water from a glass that she left there each night in anticipation of her dry-mouthed awakening.

Dave pulled the duvet over him and his breathing continued to rumble on. Sarah had never mentioned this dream to him. She had got used to her nightly journey and while it disturbed her, it no longer frightened her. She was disturbed by the loneliness and vulnerability of that person on the ledge. She was so alone and frightened. Sarah wanted to rescue her, to make her safe, but it is impossible to reach her, to even offer a word of comfort. The fact that that person is herself made the situation even more desperate. Sarah wanted to rescue herself, but was powerless to do so. She lay back onto her pillow and turned towards her husband, nestling against his back for warmth. She returned to sleep knowing that the remaining two hours would pass peacefully. All was well – or at least as well as it could be.

Sarah had always felt lucky. Of course Karl, now 11, had his problems, but he was her son. He was funny, caring and protective. He was all the things any woman could wish for in a son. Some people had "able-bodied" children who presented them with all kinds of problems. She couldn't imagine how Trev and Gill coped with their son Andrew. Now that was trouble. Drug-taking, stealing, stopping out late without letting them know where he was or whether he was safe. She knew she wouldn't have the patience to deal with that.

She also had two other wonderful children who were a delight. Now eight years old, James never failed to be helpful. His patience with the demands of his elder brother often drew comments from neighbours and friends. He was not a saint, but he was a good little boy.

He made her smile. He was blessed with a very witty sense of humour, but that wasn't why she smiled when she thought of him. She smiled because his very presence made her happy. Comfy was a better word. Yes he made her feel comfy and she liked feeling comfy.

She had no complaints about her eldest, Melanie. She could have had her nose put out by the demands that Karl put on her parents.

They always worried that she might lose out, but she showed no signs of thinking like that. Melanie had shown from an early age that she understood the situation. She was a tremendous source of 'girls together' support for her mum and Sarah was immensely proud of her. Yes, she was very lucky. She thought she was the luckiest woman alive, but she was to see this ripped apart.

It is often the case that families with a severely disabled person have multiple problems. These problems can take a variety of forms. Often families struggle for money if a wage earner is affected, or if one of the parents has to stop work in order to look after a dependent child. Sometimes it can be that a sibling cannot cope with another receiving a disproportionate amount of time, and develops behavioural problems often associated with attention seeking.

Sometimes if there is a genetic problem, more than one person in the family has a problem requiring care or help of some kind or other. Whatever the problem is, people with disabilities or rather families with disabilities have problems beyond their control. Nevertheless, the response of society is often pitiful, if not downright neglectful. In Karl's case, he began to need a wheelchair when he was nine. By the time he was 11 he had become so weak that he needed an electric wheelchair.

These machines are not cheap, costing around £2,500, depending on the type required. They are not funded automatically by the Health Service, social services or the Benefits Agency. People, young kids who can no longer walk, for whom feeding has meant a return to the physical needs of a baby; people with a sense of dignity who need to wear a nappy and have their bottoms cleaned by others have no automatic right to an electric wheelchair. They have to meet certain criteria. If they want a wheelchair which is better than the basic one they have to pay. This is often impossible without fund-raising. Often families like Karl's struggle because they only have one wage earner and extra costs. It was this need for money that brought Sarah's life to a complete halt on a chilly 11 November 2003.

Dave had been working overtime at the pit and had just done a 13-hour shift. He didn't want overtime. He was needed at home, but at the same time he couldn't turn the money down. Non-stop production meant that machines always needed some maintenance or other. As a fitter, he was always in demand and sometimes if a machine was halting coal production he had to stay until it was working again. Dave had just left the main entrance of the pit. It was 7.10am. Overhead, the sky was still black, but further in the distance its colour turned to deep blue. As he drove up Welton Moor Road he could see a sliver of red merged with green and grey as daylight broke. Reaching the top, he descended rapidly down the hill. When he reached the bottom he turned right onto a quiet dual carriageway. Suddenly, as the warmth from the heater drove the chill from his feet and crept up his legs, he began to feel the effects of his long night 1,000 feet under the town. Undeterred, he carried on. He was tired, but it would only take another 25 minutes.

Until the previous year his journey to work had only taken 10 minutes, but after his pit closed down he had been transferred to Queen's Colliery 10 miles further away. Beggars couldn't be choosers and so, like most of his colleagues, he'd moved to this new super pit. Now there were rumours circulating that this pit was to close. So many worries and so many demands. Dave always worked hard. He hadn't had a day off sick in seven years. Too many bills were accompanied by too little sleep. Sarah bore the brunt of caring for Karl and he tried to do as much he could. But working as a miner on shifts took the energy from him. He was always tired.

"Maybe I'll have a day off soon, turn it into a long weekend," he thought. Not long now, only 15 minutes and then a cup of tea, a bacon sandwich, a warm bath and bed.

Dave was thinking such pleasant thoughts when he felt a loud thud underneath the car. Then he saw sparks from the front and realised he was on the central barrier. Before he could react the car was careering leftwards and hit something. The effect was to thrust the wheels rightward with tremendous force. This spun his steering wheel violently rightwards, propelling him like a rag doll against his door and bursting the lock. The impact ripped his seat belt from its mounting and he landed on the tarmac as the car bounced off the barrier for a second time and sped towards the banking on the left.

Dave was aware of everything. Feeling no pain he lay on the road He could hear the car overturn and heard its metal scraping along the surface. He heard the faint explosion as it caught fire and he could see the gentle glow of the flames reflected on the barrier. Soon he became aware of noises; people, sirens, vehicles coming to a halt. He closed his eyes and then he saw her walking towards him.

Slowly, almost ghostlike, with the light of vehicle headlights behind her, she appeared almost heavenly. She was beautiful. As beautiful as the day they had been married. Her dark brown hair shone with a hint of red. It was tied back and swept up into a stylish bun, revealing a slender neck that invited a tender loving kiss. She wore a thin cotton top that sat off her shoulders. As she moved her breasts swayed softly and gently. Without effort or noise of any kind, she lay down beside him. Not speaking, she faced him and smiled. Her smile was calming and he felt himself smile.

They lay there for ages staring into each other's eyes. They talked about their life together. Sarah told him how grateful she was for her three lovely children. She thanked him for his support and his tireless effort, for his reliability and steadfastness. She thanked him for his love and her pleasure and all the time she smiled. As she lay there, resting on her left arm with her hand supporting her chin he marvelled at her simple beauty. He told her that he loved her. She smiled again.

He tried to reach for her but somehow he couldn't summon the energy. He tried once more but she pushed him gently back and stroked his forehead with the back of her hand. He tried to speak, but that failed too. She put her finger to her lips and seductively motioned him to be quiet.

"You need your rest." she said, once more stroking his forehead. He couldn't quite work out what the blue glow that surrounded her was, but it added warmth to the atmosphere. For a while neither spoke a word and yet he felt as one with her. She told him that she would be alright and that somehow she would manage. He didn't understand.

"Manage?"

"Yes, I'll manage. Don't worry my love. There's no need to worry."

He wanted to ask how she would manage. Where was he going? Why would he leave? She needed him. They were a team. He tried to speak again but his strength failed completely

Suddenly, peace came over him. He wanted to say much more to her. He wanted to say how he'd never leave her. He wanted to say how proud he was of her courage. He wanted to tell her that he loved her. As he gathered all his strength she spoke to him. Her last words to him were "I love you". His last words to her were "I'm sorry".

5.   An Inspector calls

Inspector Steve Morgan parked his Vauxhall Omega patrol car outside 8, Dunster Close. The house was just an ordinary house just like any other on this estate.

He sat there and paused for a moment. Beside him sat PC Julie Adams, who had been a police officer for just over a year. "I've been doing this job for over 20 years and I'm still not used to this." He looked at her almost imploringly and for a sickening moment Julie thought that he was going to ask her to do the talking. Thankfully he then said "When we go in, I'll do all the talking. Just stick with me. If she needs a cup of tea or anything..."

He paused and she understood. She nodded, but neither spoke as they got out of the car. Young women, taking children to school eyed them, half smiling, half with suspicion. Two hesitated, looking backwards as the police officers walked down the path of number eight, before resuming their journey. Before he realised it, Inspector Morgan had entered official mode and knocked on the front door.

After a second knock had failed to gain a response he was contemplating a third when he heard a child shout "Mam. There's a policeman at the front door."

Immediately he could see through the beaten glass panel a figure coming down the stairs. Morgan prepared to speak.

The door opened and a woman in her 30s stood before him. She wore a pale purple top and dark purple slacks. Over these she wore a white translucent apron, like the ones in hospitals and on her hands latex gloves.

"Yes?"

"Mrs Burgess?"

"Yes? What's the matter? What's wrong?"

Seeing the obvious panic he said, "May we come in?"

"Oh my God, why? What's happened to Dave? What's happened?"

Almost forcing their way in he took her gently by the elbow. Just then a voice shouted for his mother.

"My son Karl. He's just out of the bath. He's disabled."

"Is there anyone who can help?"

"Me mother. She lives across the street." Sarah turned to James who was standing silently at his mother's side.

"Pet. Go and tell nana June that she's needed and to come right now."

"Why what's wrong? There was fear in the boy's voice.

"Just tell nana June to come straight away. And mind the road!"

She watched after her youngest child, a little messenger carrying one of the most important messages of his life. And then she turned to

24

Morgan. At first she was silent, looking into his eyes with an unspoken question waiting for an unspoken answer.

Morgan was uncertain. This was a very awkward situation. Normally he would walk in, face an apprehensive relative, and tell them to sit down and then deliver the bad news as solemnly as possible before talking about support and arrangements.

Here the officers were in a situation where the wife knew something catastrophic had befallen her and her family and yet she still didn't know what it was, but to tell her in the hallway while she waited for help with her son was undignified. Yet, not saying anything meant that the disaster was becoming more obvious and painful by the minute. Then she solved the dilemma for him.

"It's Dave isn't it?"

"Mum!"

Morgan stared at her and was about to speak.

"Mum!"

She wrenched her head towards the voice that came from the rear of the house.

"Coming."

She turned to him "Is he dead?"

He paused.

"Answer me". She hissed, trying to avoid Karl hearing them.

Morgan looked at her. Her eyes were intense and wide. She had no time for kindness.

"I'm so sorry, Mrs Burgess. I really am."

She stared at him.

"Mum!"

"It's okay," she said, her lips hardly seeming to move as she spoke. "I'll just see to my son" and with that she withdrew into the back room where Karl lay on the settee wrapped in a bath towel with a hand towel around his head.

"What's up?"

"Er. Dad's had an accident"

"What kind of accident?"

"I'm not sure yet. I need talk to the police officers."

"Is he all right?"

She looked at Karl her eyes big and wet and vulnerable.

"Tell me."

"I don't know," she cried.

"Come in officer" she shouted.

Inspector Steve Morgan shuffled his 23 years of police experience into the room. Before him, on a settee lay a young boy, with the face and attitude of a man. At the side of the settee was parked a wheelchair and on the wall were pictures of a woman, he recognised as the mother, and two men. One he presumed to be the boy's father while the other showed a man in rugby kit.

"What's happened?" shouted the boy.

The mother looked at the officer. Her eyes pierced into him. She said nothing, waiting for an answer to her son's question. It was obvious that she couldn't leave the boy unattended. This was a very unusual way of doing it but. Morgan cleared his throat.

"I am very sorry to tell you that Mr Dave Burgess was involved in a road accident at approximately 7.30 this morning."

"And?"

"I'm afraid he has since died."

As he spoke these words there was a gasp from the hallway as Sarah's mother who had just entered the house with James heard the news. Instinctively, she grabbed the child's coat and drew him to her, holding his head to her side as if trying to make sure that the words already spoken would not be heard.

Sarah, who had been silent, burst into tears when she heard her mother's voice. Suddenly Sarah was a child and the cry brought a mother's hug and a mother's hug can make normally bad things go away, but it wasn't going to this time.

Karl lay crying on the couch, his mother wrapped in her mother's arms and James stood trembling in the corner until PC Adams took his hand and led him to his mum. All four of them held each other, oblivious to the two police officers who could only stand and watch.

Morgan had told his sidekick for the week what to expect, but even he had not expected what was before him now. He had witnessed some pretty awful moments, but he'd never felt so bad. This was a vulnerable family. The child was helpless and the mother, the main carer, had lost her source of support. It took some time before they asked the next question, which was predictably what had happened?

Morgan explained that there had been no witnesses. The road had been quiet. According to the police at the scene it looked as if he'd drifted, asleep, into the central barrier before careering back towards the side banking whereupon the car turned over. Dave was dead when the ambulance and police arrived.

"It would have been quick."

Sarah's eyes stared at Morgan and he felt foolish. He always told relatives that in an attempt to make them feel better, but it never did. If he was honest, he probably said it to make himself feel better. In all his 23 years as a police officer he'd never come to terms with the difficulties of telling someone that a loved one had died. A death of a child was always worst, then it was the death of a partner. He always sat there in silence, waiting for the relative to gather themselves. He watched as grandmother cuddled mother and one son while holding the hand of the other child who was sat in the chair. "Would you like me to make you a cup of tea?" asked Morgan.

No one said anything. The grandmother just stood there with one eye peering from the back of her daughter's head.

"Hush, hush"

Morgan looked at Adams and his eyes motioned her to go into the kitchen. She went into a narrow long room that could have passed for a corridor. She had to learn how to deal with different situations, but for now she was relieved to get out of the room.

She opened cupboards at the bottom, but found pots and pans. Next to it she found plates and breakfast dishes. Adams was trying not to make a noise. She always found it annoying when she couldn't find things and had to ask for help three or four times. But now asking for help didn't seem appropriate. This was not a regular social gathering. The next cupboard had mugs and cups.

"In the top left hand cupboard above the washer", shouted the grandma. Morgan went in to help, relieved that he had an excuse to get away from the traumatic scene.

The two officers didn't say anything as they made the tea. A half look conveyed the feeling of tension. "Poor buggers," he whispered. "They look like they've got enough on their plate without this. Look at this kitchen. They've not got two pennies to rub together."

Adams was silent, busying herself with tea bags cups and bottles of milk. Morgan could tell she was upset. He had done his best, but he had not been prepared for this himself. He stood there, anxious to support his junior as well as the family until the police support unit arrived. He decided that the best way to help her was to say as little as possible. The family would direct the conversation. They would probably want questions answered anyway. They returned with the cups of tea.

"I knew something was wrong. He's often late with his job, but he always rings, rang." There was a pause as the significance of the change in tense hit her. "He always rang," she whispered. "I knew something was wrong." Her hands shook and she spilt her tea. Her mother took it from her and put it on a side table while she composed herself.

Anxious to deal with practical issues as a way of getting her to talk lucidly, Morgan began to talk about identification and the arrival of the police liaison officer. He explained all the procedures that would take place. A police family liaison officer would be assigned to her; there would have to be a formal identification and a post-mortem and an inquest. Only then would there be a funeral.

"Oh no, no, no, no, no" she spluttered.

"Sarah."

"Oh no, no, no, no."

27

Sarah's mum told the police officers that she would deal with it and that perhaps it was best if they left. Morgan and Adams needed no excuse and left with the details they required.

In the car, Morgan eased into his seat and sighed. Constable Adams shut her door as he fastened his seat belt slowly, almost painfully. He moved as if he'd just done 15 rounds with Mike Tyson. He gave out another sigh. The rookie looked at the man who was supposed to be setting an example.

"It doesn't get any easier then."

"What do you think?"

"I don't know which is worse, dealing with the mess on the road or the mess in the house."

There was a pause.

"No you're right. It doesn't get any easier, but sometimes it's worse than others." He looked towards the front door as if he could see what was going on behind it.

"How the hell will she cope?" With that he turned on the ignition. He radioed in to the control room that he was available once more. As the car slowly pulled away he said: "Let's go for a cup of tea."

She sat there all day with her children and her mother holding the card the police officer had given her. She ate nothing. Mum saw to the kids. Another police officer came later on and spoke to her mother about arrangements and support that was available to her. None of it registered. Mum would have to deal with it.

After the police had finally left and the light began to fade from the day, mum made some tea assisted silently by Melanie who had been brought home from school. The kids ate some of it, but not Sarah. Outside children played. Street lights came on as the children disappeared indoors to prepare for bed and the street became quiet. A middle aged couple strolled by, on their way to a pleasant evening in the pub. Two hours later they passed by once more, returning home. Life carried on as normal, unaware of the trauma behind the door at number eight.

6.   The funeral

That night and for several following nights, mum stayed over and dad kept popping in to help with the kids.

Her parents were excellent. They lived across the way and had always been available to help throughout her adult life. They were there for her whenever she needed them.

They all went to the inquest. They sat there, listening to police and medical reports. There were no witnesses to the accident. There were no faults on the vehicle that could explain the loss of control. Dave had not suffered a heart attack or anything like that. Finally, the coroner concluded that Dave had fallen asleep at the wheel and that the cause of death would be classified as an accident.

The funeral took place five days later. It was a wonderful occasion, if funerals can be wonderful. A watery December sun watched the hearse draw up outside the main entrance to the crematorium. Attendants took out the coffin, placed it on to the trolley and waited to wheel it in. Behind the hearse sat the first limousine. In it Sarah was flanked by Melanie and James. Sarah's mum sat opposite and all through the journey from the house mum had sat holding their hands, talking softly. The second vehicle was the family's people carrier, especially adapted for Karl. Sarah's dad applied the handbrake, disembarked and began moving Karl and his wheelchair out of the rear of the vehicle. As he did so, grandad John cast an anxious eye to the vehicle in front. No one seemed to be getting out.

At one point it seemed like they wouldn't get Sarah here at all. Her mother had practically had to dress her. The children were lost, needing comfort and reassurance that their mother was unable to provide. John and June had acted as parents to all them. For the time being they had four children.

That morning they had simply told their children what to do and they had followed their instructions. When the hearse arrived Sarah had stood bolt upright and almost passed out. They had tried to sit her down, but she had insisted that she was okay. As she stepped out onto the path she inhaled deeply. He had grabbed her arm, but she had refused it and led her children into the limousine. His daughter was near to collapse, but she was trying hard to maintain her self-control and dignity.

John lowered Karl onto the drive. Setting the brakes he turned to replace the ramps into the rear of the car. As he locked the doors and took off Karl's brakes, he looked once more at the front limousine and to his relief a door opened. Sarah stepped out followed by the others. His daughter looked at him and he gave a reassuring nod.

"Okay?"

"Okay." A puff of breath shot from her and dissipated into the winter air. Sarah summoned all her strength. She was not going to let her husband down.

Later, she vaguely remembered being pleased at the number who had turned out. "Dave would have been impressed." She half smiled to herself. He would have joked at things like this. He always joked. Sometimes she wished he'd shut up. Now she wished she could hear something silly. Anything instead of this.

The large crowd stood waiting outside. As they assembled her children remained close to her. Sarah acknowledged no one as she followed the coffin in. The rest of the assembly entered after her. The hall was full. Even the balcony was full. Family and friends, neighbours, members of the rugby club and his workmates had all turned out in force.

Sarah was aware of them, but focused on reaching her seat at the front. She reached it without having taken a breath. She put her hand out on to the bench to steady herself as she sat down and heard herself gasp with the effort. James and Mel sat down beside her and her dad brought Karl round so that his wheelchair stood just to her left ensuring that he did not obstruct her view of the coffin. Her mum and dad sat at each side of them and they all held hands.

Funerals involving the parents of young children are always very difficult. The children needed the care and protection of the other parent, but Sarah was in no position to give it. She was as a child, helpless, in need of protection, vulnerable. Her parents cared for everyone.

At the reception Sarah managed to talk to a few people. Then it was all over. Leaving their daughter's house to return to their own was the most difficult thing that John and June had done, but they both knew that Sarah would have to be left alone some time. As they closed the front gate, June looked at her daughter and gave her a soft smile.

"You know where we are."

Sarah nodded.

They came round every day. They saw to everything and talked. Sarah was glad of their company, but within a week she had decided that she would have to deal with the situation. She would have to get life going again. She couldn't be relying on mum and dad all the time and they wouldn't be able to look after Karl for too long. It was hard work and they weren't getting any younger. It was her job and she had made a decision. It was time to get on with it. She was, should be, too busy to mope and she wasn't going to any longer.

They were putting up Christmas decorations, trying to push the children into some kind of normality, when Sarah suddenly said to her mum that she could manage by herself. Mum stood at the doorway. She turned to her daughter.

"I'm all right. Honestly. I wouldn't lie to you."

"Are you sure?" her mum asked, relieved that her daughter seemed to becoming to terms with her loss but worried about whether she was going to cope.

"Absolutely, I have to get on. There's too much to do and the kids need me. I know that Dave would want me to make sure that they are alright, and that's what I'm going to do."

"You've always been a good girl Sarah. You always were strong." They stood there, a kind, warm silence embraced them.

"If you need me."

"I know where you live."

"I'll see you in the morning." As she closed the wooden gate behind her, her mother faced her daughter.

"Thanks."

"Night, night."

With a half smile her daughter replied "Night night, mother."

"Night, night" was the expression her mother had used all her life to say goodnight. It was comforting, a confirmation that she was still loved.

Sarah stood and watched her mother cross the road, pass through her gate before climbing the seven concrete steps to her front door. Before entering her house she turned and waved to her daughter. It was a wave which said "I'm okay" but it was also a wave which whispered "I'll watch over you, you know" and then she was gone.

Sarah saw her mother's door close and for the first time since Dave's death she was alone. She stood on her front step, arms folded around a thick black cardigan. The weather had been dry, sunny and cold for nearly a fortnight, but now rain began to fall gently on the dry ground. It fell slowly at first, but quickly increased in intensity. Sarah stayed there for a few minutes listening to the sounds around her. Behind her, Karl was in his bedroom on his computer, while Mel and James were watching a video.

A car struggled up the hill, passed her and disappeared round the bend at the top, leaving her to the sound of the rain that was now beginning to run down the gutters and gurgle into the drains. Across the street, lights began to appear in front rooms in response to the gathering darkness. Front doors opened and parents called to children to come in. She took some deep breaths. Life was carrying on. She stood there, leaning on the door frame looking at the bare rose bushes in the garden, One by one the doors closed and the street fell silent. Sarah felt a shiver come over her. She stood straight, took a final look as if she were reluctant to leave and went in. She stood in the hall and closed the door and leant with her back against it. The hallway had suddenly become dark and was lit only by a sliver of light that had sneaked out of the gap between the lounge door and its frame.

In the dim light she could hear her children. Soon she would have to check on Karl's wellbeing, but she needed a moment for herself. Now the well-wishers had gone and life had begun to resume an air of normality. The problem was that she wasn't certain what normality was going to look like. She had been the strong one of the family. The one able to deal with the difficulties of caring for a disabled son, but Dave had always been there helping her, doing all the things that she decided were necessary. He had never flinched in his role of breadwinner and provider, but now things had changed and she could not yet see how those changes would affect her and her children. She paused to steady herself, and went into the kitchen to make a cup of tea. She sat on her own. The house already sounded different. There was no hammering, no sawing of wood. She couldn't hear the kids being teased.

She had seen his body. She had been to his funeral. She had been surrounded by friends and loved ones who had talked about him, yet it was only now as she heard the silence and looked at the empty chair facing her that she suddenly realised he wasn't there. Now she felt the emptiness inside her.

She heard Karl's voice. He needed her and she stirred from her isolation. She had something to do. Caring for Karl would give meaning to her life. She stood up, braced herself and went upstairs.

Across the road in her front room, the lace curtain was let loose and it fell back into place as a mother, unknown to her daughter, watched over her.

7.   Moving house

Sarah had had no choice. She had realised that while sitting in the kitchen, drinking that first cup of tea by herself. She would either sink or swim. She knew that Dave would want her to carry on, raise their children and look after Karl. In reality there was no other option. She simply had to get on with life. If the choice was to sink or swim, it was Karl's growing dependency that acted as her life jacket. She became so busy she had little time to mourn. She and Dave had had such a sweet life. They had created a lovely family life and she was determined not to let it fall apart.

Four years had now passed since David's death and Karl was now 15. Obviously, the children had grown, but Karl had both grown and declined. He had become much weaker and had been confined to a wheelchair for some time. For the last year he had needed a better electric wheelchair. Sarah was never quite sure about how Karl felt about it. He had been very impressed with the chair when it first arrived. At the flick of a switch and the movement of a joystick he was off. Sometimes he could be downright dangerous. He would fly along in his excitement. Once, he had nearly run into old Rene, her next door neighbour. Rene had been quite upset and Sarah had had to talk to Karl, but it was difficult. In a slapstick sense it had been quite funny to watch Rene's slow arthritic amble turned into a shrieking pirouette accompanied by shopping bags moving in different directions.

Unlike his contemporaries, Karl had few moments of real physical exhilaration. He saw the upright chair with its black bulky pads, its thick headrest and small stubby wheels as a racing machine and he drove it to the limit. As he got weaker, he was less able to hold his head up for any length of time. He was fitted with a brace to hold his head against the supporting headrest and as he drove along at maximum speed, it looked as if he was being pinned to his chair by an uncalculated number of G-forces. This image was enhanced by Karl's smile, which was so wide that it looked like his mouth was being ripped from his face.

To her credit Rene was very understanding. She simply got more careful. Sarah smiled as she watched the old lady checking her front gate before venturing onto the dangerous highway that her footpath had become.

People talked about how hard her life was and it was true. Karl was very demanding, but he made her smile. He had the ability to just get on with it and while she didn't want him to hurt anyone, she didn't want to stop him having fun either. If people had the strength to jump out of the road, they were lucky.

While his reliance on the new electric wheelchair was a significant new factor in their lives, there were others. The chair was big. It only just got through the front door and Karl had then to be removed from it and carried to the front room or his bedroom. Sarah could no longer move him by herself and relied on the kids to help her.

She thought about Dave every day, but it was at times like this that she realised just how much she and the family missed him. Someone from social services came round to assess the house for adaptation. They could provide ramps and widen doors but, in the end, it was decided that, as she was on her own, the best solution would be to move to a bungalow. Sarah was reluctant. She had friends nearby. Her mother was across the road and Karl was happy. However, one day she nearly tripped while carrying him to the toilet and had to accept that she could no longer manage.

The council provided a purpose built bungalow at the bottom of the estate. She knew she had been lucky to get it so quickly. Most people waited for ages in great difficulties, but she had been placed at the top of the priority list and when an old lady conveniently died she took it without hesitation.

Her current house was a semidetached which stood halfway up a steep hill. At the foot of the hill, some 300 yards away, the road curved sharply to the right. The bungalow sat in a small complex to the left.

Sarah had viewed the house with Karl, Melanie, James and her mother and father. Mel had been allowed to leave work early by her new employers so that they could all see it while there was still daylight. They walked round it in silence. The viewing was a strange experience. It was a mixture of emotions. On the one hand there was a feeling of regret that they were leaving their house, not of their choice, and excitement when they saw how the property had been adapted to meet the needs of a disabled person. All rooms had wide doors. Light switches were placed at seat height. Access in and out of the front and rear of the house was by ramp. There were no steps anywhere. The kitchen had worktops that could be dropped down to chair height, although in practice this would not be required. Karl was now no longer capable of preparing a meal, but the fact that such facilities were being provided was, nevertheless, very comforting.

They also realised their luck that a place like this had become available so quickly. Each time they walked into another room their fears diminished, bit-by-bit. With a look or a sigh, an unspoken realisation grew between them that their lives would become easier.

They stepped out of the front door. Sarah looked around the immediate vicinity as if the area was completely unknown to her, but of course she knew it well. She looked back up the hill to her house and across to her mother's.

'This would be no hardship,' she thought to herself, and already the prospect of moving seemed more positive. She knew it was the right thing to do. She turned to her son: "Well?"

"Well what?"

"What do you think about the house er bungalow?"

"It's all right."

"All right?"

Karl was doing it again, disguising his feelings so that she never quite knew what he felt.

"She means what do you think? Do you want to move or not? Stop messing around. You get everything you want. Just ssss stop pissing around." James spluttered before running off.

His outburst silenced everyone. Melanie gawped in her brother's direction, then looked in embarrassment at her mother as if it were her fault. She half-raised her hand as if seeking permission to speak.

"I'll, I'll go and check he's okay." With that, she turned on her heels and ran off in the same direction as her brother before anyone had the chance to call her back.

Grandad John put his hand on Sarah's stunned shoulders and spoke quietly: "C'mon lass. He'll be alright. These are hard times for everyone. Let's go home. Mel'll bring him back when he's calmed down."

He turned to Karl: "Come on young man. Let's go home and have a think shall we?" Karl said nothing and pressed the button that whirred his motor into action. As he passed his mother he muttered to himself loudly enough for others to hear: "Anyone would think I wanted this fucking thing."

His inability to turn his head and engage anyone eye-to-eye made the comment seem more general and upsetting. His wheels drove over the kerb and the whole chair shook as it bounced onto the road. He hit the dipped kerb on the other side at full speed before skilfully steering himself round the bend and up the hill.

Sarah stared ahead as she made to call after Karl, but her father stopped her. "Leave him be love. He's just upset. Things will sort themselves out. Everyone just needs a little time."

Sarah walked slowly home with her parents. It was obvious Karl was upset, but what was significant was that she had never heard him express his feelings like that before.

Maybe time was something they didn't have. They followed Karl's speeding vehicle back up the hill. He came to a sudden halt halfway up and sat there waiting for them to catch up.

"What's going on?"

Sarah turned to him as she came alongside him. She could see he was upset. This life was not of his choosing and she knew that he was painfully aware of the burden his existence had on the others. Most of the time, they said nothing. It was as if the whole family lived in isolation from one another. They were very close and yet they had never talked about the important issues facing them. Sarah knew that had to change.

"He knows."

"Thought so."

There was a silence. Mum and son, grandma and grandad stood there.

"I'll talk to him."

"Maybe we should all talk to each other?"

Karl did not reply, he simply pushed his joystick as hard as he could. The wheels slipped under the strain as the chair tried to obey his command and accelerate up the hill. The chair skidded forward before gaining maximum speed.

They all sat in the front room, hardly speaking, waiting for James and Mel's return. Sarah glanced out of the window at every little movement. What she had hoped would have been an interesting, possibly enjoyable, family outing to look at a new house had turned into the reality it had always been, a move forced by circumstances beyond their control that threatened to disrupt family harmony.

Her parents waited for an hour and a half. They had not planned to stay that long. John wanted his tea before leaving for choir practice, but he could not leave until he knew that James was safely home. A 10 minute wait became 15 and then 20 minutes. A cup of tea took another 10. Waiting 30 minutes without a result would have been a pointless waste of time, so they waited for another 10 and then another 10 minutes. After an hour and a half John decided that it was too late for the choir, but he was hungry and his chickens needed feeding and watering. He put on his hat and coat and was about to step out the front door when Mel appeared at the front gate with a rather sheepish James in tow.

Grandad quietly put the door on the latch and shut it gently behind him. They walked towards each other and the old man held out his arms to his grandson who simply laid his head against him. For a minute they stood there in silence. John patted James and kissed him on the head.

"Are you okay?"

He nodded.

"This is very difficult for everyone. No one has got an answer to make it any easier."

The boy nodded again.

"Your mum's doing her best."

John rubbed his shoulder.

"Are you okay to go in?"

A third nod ensued.

"C'mon."

John announced their arrival as they removed their coats. Sarah flew out and grabbed her son like a lioness seizes an antelope. The big cat grabs its prey over its face and smothers it. It can't breathe, but there is no struggle as it succumbs to its fate. James's back arched under the force of her vice-like hug. His spectacles twisted off his nose and up his forehead. She released him and shook him.

"Where have you been?"

The boy pulled his glasses down and was about to reply when he was grabbed once more and the glasses and his back returned to their former position.

"You're going to bloody kill him."

Karl's voice wafted feebly from the front room through the half-open doorway. Perhaps it was her heightened emotional state, but Sarah noticed how weak his voice sounded. She smiled at Karl's eyes as they emerged through the doorway.

James looked at his mother. "I didn't mean what I said."

"It's okay."

"No, it's not, but I didn't mean it."

"I know."

James turned to his brother. "I didn't mean what I said Karl."

"Aye."

"I do think we should move don't you?"

"Aye."

"It'll be much better."

"Aye."

And with that it was decided. They would move to their new bungalow. It would be much better. Sarah was impressed with the maturity displayed by her children and how well they handled their terrible situation. However, the evening's events had shown that they were also so very, very vulnerable.

The move meant leaving their past behind. It had been a past in which they had been able to live with some degree of normality and hope. Now they were heading in only one direction and it would affect them all. The move signalled the beginning of a certain future.

8.   Knowing the score

Sarah knew that she was blessed with wonderful children. Everyone said what a credit they all were. They all marvelled at how brave Karl was and how helpful the other two were. This togetherness was obtained at a price, however.

Melanie was nearly 18 and worked in a solicitor's office. At 16 she had left school with nine GCSEs including five 'A' stars. She had no difficulty in getting a job. A local company of solicitors had snapped her up and she was gaining professional qualifications through work. Mel was highly thought of and was hoping to move on to be a legal secretary.

Her teachers at college had all suggested in the strongest possible terms that she should go to university and study law. Sarah had wanted her to, but Mel thought it was impossible. She did not feel that she could cope with the demands of studying for a degree combined with the need to work part-time to earn money to help the family.

Mum had insisted that she would not have to help with Karl in any way that might affect her studies, but Mel knew that was impossible. There was no way that mum could do everything even if she wanted to. She never had a full night's sleep, ever. Even if her mum could do it all, there was no way that she was going to let her. Karl was her younger brother and needed help.

She knew the score. Everyone could see he had started to get more demanding because he was becoming weaker. She wasn't going to avoid doing her duty towards her mum and her brother. They were going to see this out together and university could wait. How would she be able to study with everything that was about to happen in the next two or three years? She would get a job, pay her way, help her mum and look after her brother. Nothing else mattered.

As the baby of the family James had been less involved in the family's traumas. He had only discovered nine months ago, just after his 11th birthday, that his brother was terminally ill. A friend at school whose cousin had died from muscular dystrophy had mentioned it one afternoon in a history lesson. He had assumed James knew. James remembered the moment vividly. He had wanted to be sick as he sat there pinned to his seat, his head spinning. He wasn't sure about what happened next. His knowledge of what he did came later from the same friend.

Evidently he had uttered a strange gargling noise as if he were being strangled. He stood up as Mr Rees was introducing a lesson on the significance of the Roman occupation of Britain, grabbed his coat, ran out of the classroom and down the corridor with his teacher's lost commands trailing behind him. He ran the two miles home without stopping and arrived as his mother was setting out to the local shops to get something for tea. They met at the front door. Sarah could see the distress in his eyes and knew instinctively that somehow James had learnt the truth.

Of course she was going to tell him, but she had not yet found the correct moment and as time passed it seemed to get more and more difficult. It had been different with Mel. Being the oldest, she had grown up knowing what the situation was. The way they lived, the path they were all travelling down seemed to be taken for granted as if everyone knew. She had wanted to protect James and had always felt that she was managing the situation. She would have told him, but events were beginning to gather a momentum of their own and she saw in her son's twisted face that they had just caught up with her.

James now bent before her, too breathless to cry or speak, his head tilted towards the ground, his eyes lifted to her face. He gazed at her as if she had betrayed him.

"Why... didn't you... tell me?" He wheezed. "Why?"

He was leaning towards his left, his right hand steadied on his knee. His left arm swayed limply in a peculiar fashion. He tried to straighten up which was not a good thing to do as he dizzily fell backwards, crumpling in a heap onto his bottom. He lay on his back on the grass, supported by his elbows, but even this proved too much. His head arched backwards and his arms collapsed. He fell completely on to the floor, with both hands lying on his heaving chest.

Sarah sat down beside him. She tried to stroke his forehead, but he brushed her hand away. "Get off!" He coughed.

"Is he all right?"

Jenny, her next door neighbour, had popped her hair and curlers over the hedge.

"Yes, Jenny, he's just a little upset."

James gasped a snort.

"Only I heard a bit of a commotion and wondered. I mean I don't want to interfere but..."

"It's alright honestly. Things will be ok."

"Well, if you're sure"

Jenny seemed reluctant to leave. Surely she didn't think that something untoward was going on as if her son who was as tall as her was being abused in public or something?

Sarah didn't need an audience.

"I'll see you later. I'll explain things to you later."

"Aye, right then. If you are sure you're okay."

"We're fine, thank you."

Precisely what she was going to explain to the old dear was another matter, but the apparent offer of a detailed chat later on seemed to do the trick and Jenny went in. Sarah sighed.

By this time James had regained his breath, if not his strength. She looked at his eyes which appealed to her to say that it wasn't true. She put her arms round his neck and cradled his head.

"I was going to tell you, honestly I was." His appeal having been denied, James's face crumpled. Sarah held him. She kissed the top of his head and nestled her cheek against it.

"Shall we go inside? We need to talk."

With that he cried even louder, but stood up. She looked into her son's eyes. "I love you," and led the crumpled heap inside.

She sat in the kitchen, facing her youngest child. It was strange how so many significant events took place in the kitchen. It was the serious room or maybe it was simply the fact that she always handled troubled matters better when she had a cup of tea to hold on to. James's eyes focused intently on her, absorbing every word as she told him simply and directly that his big brother, albeit his sick, weak brother, was going to die and that his death would occur sometime in the next two or three years at the most. He said nothing. He didn't even blink. He just sat there, a tortured and pained little boy who was beyond the comfort and protection of a cuddle which, nevertheless, was what he needed.

Sarah finished speaking and looked at him. He remained silent, his right hand cupped in his left lay on the table. Eventually Sarah could bear it no longer and blurted half of the words "I'm sorry," before busting into tears that she quickly stopped.

They sat there in silence and then he said "It's okay. I understand." He stood up.

"Where are you going?"

"To my room."

"Would you like a drink?"

He shook his head and simply patted her shoulder in a fatherly fashion, as he left. He stayed there all afternoon listening to music played at full volume. Sarah hovered round the hallway, stairs and landing listening for sounds that indicated he was all right. She heard nothing over the din.

At 4.15pm precisely the big white bus pulled up outside their house. The routine was the same. Tony got out and opened the rear door. He and Sue moved Karl's chair onto the platform and Tony brought it down to ground level. Karl drove off and Tony reversed the procedure.

Karl was in the middle of his grand farewells when James burst forward from the house and smothered him in an enormous hug.

"I love you," cried James.

"Fuck off," replied Karl.

Karl was not pleased. The entire bus had seen him with his brother's arms wrapped around him. It spoiled his street cred and he knew tomorrow's journey would be full of ridicule.

"What you doin' you arsehole?"

Sarah did not know what to say. James stood there embarrassed. He wanted to tell his brother that he knew, but he didn't know how to and Karl never voluntarily broached the subject with anyone. He steered his vehicle past his mother and brother and entered the house still cursing his brother's behaviour. Sarah and James followed like two scolded children.

Nothing else was said. That evening the children behaved as if nothing had happened. Next day Karl survived a few comments on the bus that turned out to be far less arduous than he had imagined. The day passed, then a week without any comment, and Sarah forgot about it until James's next outburst. It was a reminder that she had to be aware of the needs of all her children in the coming months. She was frightened she might not be able to handle it on her own.

9.   The social

The move into the new bungalow had gone smoothly. As is so often the case when people are forced into change the imagined problems never arose and within a week the old house, the place of their memories became just that, a memory. There were no regrets. This was their home now. It was such an improvement on the old house. The front access was ramped. The kerb outside was lowered so that Karl could get off the bus and onto the pavement smoothly. The front garden was open plan so that there was no narrow gate to negotiate. Inside things were also much better. Doors were wide enough to take his electric wheelchair. There was a toilet which was wide enough to allow a helper to get round the side of the seat. Most importantly of all, everything was on the ground floor. Sarah no longer had to carry her son up (and just as difficult) down the stairs. At the side of Karl's bed stood a hoist which would help Sarah get him into bed, at least in the short term. She knew that eventually moving him would become a much more delicate operation, but that was in the future. For now her life and Karl's had been made much easier. Nobody gave the old house a second thought.

Except occasionally, when she visited her mother she would sometimes steal a glance. She would see herself, younger, coming out of the house with a cup of tea for Dave as he stood bent over the engine of their car. She could see herself smiling. They kissed and she trotted and skipped girlishly back to her children. Another time she could see him wrestling with the kids in the garden on a fine summer's day. He would be on his knees, topless, ready to take on all comers. She remembered his muscles, his strength and his gentleness as all three kids piled into him at once.

She smiled sadly every time she passed. She always walked on the other side of the road, partly because her mother's house stood there, but also because it allowed her to see the house in full view.

One day as she was about to open the gate to her mother's house she turned to steal a look. A young man stood in the garden with two boys. She gasped and then realised it wasn't Dave. Someone else was living there doing the things they had done. He looked up and saw her staring and she turned away, embarrassed.

The bungalow was better. It met their practical needs, but it was not the place where they had formed a life together. For a while she had kept the house and its memories alive in her head despite no longer living there. Only now did she understand that it belonged to someone else. It had taken her months to come to this realisation and the force of it shook her. She missed the house. She missed him. She stood trembling at the gate and jumped when her mother's gentle hand touched her shoulder.

"Penny for them."

"What?"

"Your thoughts."

"Oh yes. I was just..."

"Remembering?"

Sarah nodded silently.

"Are you coming in? I've just made a lovely pot of tea."

Sarah smiled. Her mother's cups of tea had solved many a problem over the years. Whether they would help her to put the past where it belonged and help her build a future was another matter.

Although the social services department had managed to place them in their new home very quickly, it soon became apparent that they had acted with not a moment to spare.

Karl's physical condition had declined. He had noticeably lost weight and continually complained of being tired. He also got frequent bedsores from sitting in the same position all day. As he lost weight his ability to stay comfortable became limited. He didn't have the padding on his body to cushion himself. At first this resulted in him constantly shifting his position to try and get comfortable but by his 16th birthday he was less able to move himself, a sure sign that he was weakening. At first Sarah tried to ignore it, but it was becoming undeniable.

After a meeting with the technical services support unit at the school it was agreed that Karl needed a new chair. He was entitled to a wheelchair, provided by the National Health Service, but it was limited. He was only entitled to a basic chair which meant that he would lose more of his independence.

It was decided to buy a chair privately. Sarah hated doing this. She didn't see why her son wasn't entitled to the best. "After all it wasn't as if he'd be using it long enough to wear it out," she said to herself once as she washed dishes.

Then she realised the implications of this thought and shook her head as if doing so would throw the thought away. She found herself grasping the edge of the sink. After a few moments she took a deep breath and carried on washing dishes. It occurred to her that that was what she seemed to be doing a lot recently. Taking deep breaths was becoming a normal, even a daily occurrence. As she washed the last cup and wiped down the sink and worktop she thought to herself, "He's going to have the best."

She'd seen what the best was. It had heavily padded cushioning to sit on with side panels that were moulded to keep his body in a stable position. A head rest would hold his head up because it was becoming more difficult for him to do it himself as the months passed and his muscles weakened. The problem was that she had no way of raising the money. She still owed money on the loan for his present chair and her parents were in no position to help.

A family meeting planned out a series of fund raising events. The main one was to be a social at the local rugby league club that Dave had played for and Karl's uncles still did.

"I'll ask the choir if they'll do a show as well," said her dad.

"Will they do that? I thought they only performed to raise money for charities?"

"Well, what do you call this? Anyway they have done performances to assist members before. We did a little show at George Green's niece's wedding last year."

"If they can do something for that, they can do something for Karl. I'm sure they will."

"Er" Karl piped up.

"Yes love?"

"Can we invite Chris Anderton?"

"Why do you want him to come? I think he'd be too busy anyway."

"Well, people might come if he was the guest of honour and we'd raise more money."

"I'm not sure."

"There's no harm in trying lass" joined in her father. "You know he's the lad's hero. His grandad is in the choir. I'll ask him. I'm sure he will do it if he's free."

Sarah did not seem keen, but none of the others could understand her objections. Chris was the star of the town's professional rugby league club and his presence would be certain to assure a good attendance from the amateur club's players and supporters. Dave had been well respected in rugby league and the professional club had promised assistance to his family when he died.

Sarah's family did not know that she found the prospect of meeting Chris Anderton difficult. She knew perfectly well who he was, but the problem was that he reminded her of Dave.

She had not had any kind of relationship with a man since Dave's death. She had not had the time. Looking after Karl had occupied her every waking moment and her sleeping ones as well. She often had to get up in the middle of the night to see to his needs. Sarah had always felt so tired. No there was no question. There would be plenty of time after...

She closed her eyes. That was the second time she had thought in terms of life after Karl. She was beginning to anticipate the inevitable and that meant that it was going to happen. She had always tried to live for the present and blot out other thoughts and possibilities.

Gradually and without warning the future was beginning to impose itself on the present and it troubled her.

She thought of the photograph on Karl's wall. It showed Anderton scoring a try for Castleton. Karl had followed them ever since he was eight. His dad had taken him to every home game that work commitments would allow. Karl was very knowledgeable. He knew all about the game's history, famous players, the lot. After Dave had gone, she or his grandad had taken Karl to as many games as possible, trying to keep life as normal as possible. She had noticed him. She thought he was very attractive in a curious mixture of roughness and gentleness, just like Dave. As soon as she found herself thinking like that she snuffed out any further thoughts. She was not going to betray Dave, and anyway she didn't have the time. And so she continued like that for more than four years, alone and busy.

"Alright, I don't suppose it'll do any harm to ask."

"Yeaahhh!" shouted Karl softly.

"Aw, cool mum, thanks."

Her father smiled.

"I'll see his grandad tomorrow."

"Are you coming tomorrow?"

John turned to Karl who often accompanied his grandad to choir.

"Yeah. Wouldn't miss that music for the world."

With that the family meeting concluded.

Karl had hope.

His mother had misgivings.

In the middle of the night at two in the morning, or at three or sometimes at daybreak she lay awake, sometimes all night. She tried desperately to go to sleep, because she needed to rest and yet she did not, could not. In those quiet hours she lay wrapped in her duvet, hiding from the cold and life.

She wished her husband would put his arm around her just once and warm her like he used to do. She remembered how she would lie there in a ball as his arms enveloped her. She would sigh and keep her eyes shut. He was so strong, and yet so gentle. He would hold her and his kisses would move down from her neck and along her shoulders. His hands would stroke the sides of her arms tenderly and she would smile to herself in anticipation. She would turn to him and he would whisper "I love you". She remembered how he always managed to make it sound just as sweet as he had on their first time, when she had felt a glow and a pleasure she could not have imagined possible. That feeling had never left her. She longed to feel it one more time, just once more. She wanted to feel protected as she protected others.

It was not too much to ask. She smiled at the thought of him and then her smile faded with the realisation that there will never be another time. She did not cry. She was too sad to cry. As a child she often wondered what the expression 'an aching heart' actually meant. How could a heart ache? Now, she understood.

Her heart ached.

Her body ached.

Her soul ached.

At some time she drifted to sleep; the sleep of the abandoned; of the lonely; of the desperate. She needed to rest.

Each night it was the same. Each night, all she wanted was something she could not have. In her room, inside the shelter of her duvet, she lay alone, missing him. She did not tell anyone, because no one could make it better. No one could bring him back. Her sorrow must stay locked inside. She must remain strong for others and so, she shared her pain with no one. Each day to rise, exist and tell no one.

10. John Black was late

Grandad John Black was late. He hated being late for anything. It made him feel anxious and at his age, he didn't like feeling anxious. Most of all he hated being late for the choir. He had been a member of the Castleton male voice choir for 27 years. It had always been important to him and now, in his retirement, it was one of the focal points of his life. He rarely missed a rehearsal and had, to his recollection, never missed a performance. Ten years ago, he had been elected to the committee. He was proud of that. He was proud of the choir. It was one of the leading choirs in Britain, and certainly one of the best in Yorkshire.

But tonight he was late. He passed the Victorian Town Hall. He turned left off Victoria Square into Baxter Street, passing down the right hand side of the Town Hall. The people carrier rose and fell over the sleeping policeman that had been put in place over the last couple of years to slow the traffic. He heard Karl grunt in the back.

"Sorry" he said.

As they approached the next one, he slowed right down to minimise the effect. If he went too slowly the vehicle would jerk as it began to stall. If he went too quickly the effect over the bumps would be the same. Karl would grunt.

Karl was really chuffed at first when he had got his current chair. He thought it was fantastic. He could get about at school and on the street. It gave him full mobility at the push of a switch but, and it was a big but, it had also become his prison. He could no longer move without it and it was becoming uncomfortable. He had lost weight and the padding was now inadequate. It no longer gave him the support he needed. That's why he needed a new one that was stronger and a bit slower. Karl liked going fast, but he had started to feel all the bumps and he couldn't move fast enough to control it anymore. He hadn't told anyone, but its speed was starting to frighten him.

Now he sat in the chair in the back of the carrier. It had been specially converted so that floor mountings secured the chair and stopped him sliding. He was safe, but he so wished that he could sit alongside grandad like in the old days.

"Here we go!" shouted John as the vehicle rose and fell once more. Karl grunted yet again. There were five sets of bumps before the left-hand turn into the church entrance. Karl knew and felt every one of them. At first it had been a bit of a joke.

He'd complain about, "those bloody coppers lying down on the job," but gradually the jokes had stopped. At first, they had been replaced by curses, but now he simply grunted. John had noted the change in his grandson. Things were getting worse.

He tried to be cheerful with Karl. He was always cheerful, but underneath, John sighed to himself and concentrated on the task in hand. He enjoyed his grandson's company every Wednesday evening, but it was getting increasingly difficult to manage. He felt every bump as well and cursed his poor driving, but there was nothing to be done.

When their son-in-law died he and his wife, June had promised each other that they would dedicate their lives to helping their daughter deal with what was to come and they had never flinched from that. He had continued to take Karl to watch his beloved rugby team, sometimes with Sarah. Every Wednesday he brought Karl with him to the choir. He liked the journey. It was special, a time for a grandad to be alone with his grandson. There was a quiet gentleness in Karl's manner that was strangely soothing, but he so wished that he could sit alongside him like he used to do.

He turned left into the church's car park. He steered to the right, before reversing to the left towards the entrance of the church hall. He manoeuvred into the spaces left by the other choir members.

Everyone was so considerate. They all knew the routine. Each week they left the spaces for them. Karl was their pet. They looked out for him.

The brake lights glowed against the heavy wooden doors as John brought the vehicle to a halt. He switched off and carefully checked that the handbrake was on. There was no room for error. He left his seat and checked the brake once more. As he closed his door he gave one final look. The vehicle must not move. Opening the back doors, he reached inside for the ramps down which the chair would exit. John secured them onto the lips at the rear and dropped them gently onto the floor. The lips were positioned at the correct width, but he still checked them and lined them up with the wheels of the chair. On no occasion in the two years that he had been doing this had he needed to alter the ramps' positions, but still he checked them. They mustn't move. John grunted as he levered himself into the back of the carrier.

"You sound worse than I do" said Karl.

"It's bloody awkward doing this at my age."

"Well at least I'll never be as old and decrepit as you."

They laughed. John busied himself undoing the straps.

"Right then, back up slowly."

He lent his hand against the rear of the chair as Karl reversed, but Karl had good control. Nevertheless, they mustn't slip. Casting one quick eye in the direction of the handbrake, John said "Righto".

The wheelchair moved backwards and began to tip. John steadied it as the wheels slowly rolled down to the tarmac. Checking he was clear, Karl swung his vehicle round towards the door while John put away the ramps and locked up.

John opened the big front door. Karl entered and swung to the right into the narrow corridor. Barging through the half open door they were hit by a wall of sound as 50 male voices reached towards the climax of *Nessun Dorma*.

Karl headed across the front of the choir to the kitchen where he helped Carol prepare the teas for break time. As he passed, the conductor smiled and shortened his arm movements to avoid hitting him. Choir members gingerly removed their feet from danger without breaking pace and tune. It happened every week. John quickly removed his hat and coat and joined in the rehearsal.

Carol was a large woman who had served teas at the break for the last 10 years. Her husband Fred had been a member until his death four years ago. Carol had simply kept up the routine. She looked forward to seeing Karl. He had always been bright and cheerful and Wednesdays always made her feel better. At first Karl had helped to get the cups out and pour the tea. Then, when he was confined to his chair she carefully placed cups on his tray and he would help serve. Recently, however, he had stopped bothering and she now served everyone from the hatch.

Karl simply wanted a chat and a routine. In many ways, he was just like her. He was surviving and there was nothing better to lift the spirits than a good sing-song. Although she doubted if a youngster like Karl would agree with her, she enjoyed the music. They sang all kinds of music: opera, hymns, ballads, songs and musicals. She often sang along as she boiled the water, taking care not to sing too loudly, but she doubted whether she would be heard anyway. Nevertheless, she kept her voice under control as she prepared for break time. Occasionally, when they were not talking, she would steal a glance at this young man who said that he didn't like the music.

"It's for old codgers."

But she often thought she heard him humming as he sat and watched from the corner of the room. One song that he definitely paid attention to was a beautiful song called *Here you'll find a haven*. It was not well known, but the choir sung it at their charity events. It was a gentle song about life in a hospice, about facing up to life and dealing with what was given to you. It wasn't a sad song. In fact, it was a very strong, positive song and whenever they sang it he would stop talking and listen and then be quiet for a while. She watched him and wanted to hold him, to make things better. Then the song would finish. She would wipe half a tear from her eye, they would return to their duties and cheer each other up. Karl always made her feel better. He was the toughest little boy she had ever met.

Every Wednesday choir practice finished at 9.30pm precisely. Tonight was slightly different for at 9.20pm Karl noticed a large figure enter and sit down at the back of the room. He recognised him immediately. It was Chris Anderton. Karl double-checked, but he was right. He was sitting there.

Anderton was a local lad who played for his local team since he was 18. He had studied his 'A' levels at school and was planning to go to university, but Castleton had stepped in with an offer that was too good to turn down. He had recognised that turning his back on higher education was a risk, but had decided that if things didn't work out with rugby league, he could always return to his studies.

He was proud of his local roots and had never wished to move to any of the sport's bigger clubs. He was paid well enough and many said that, because he was now moving towards his retirement, there would be a bright future for him as a coach.

He wasn't greedy and didn't feel the need to move. He liked his life. Occasionally when he was free he would nip to the choir at the end of rehearsal to meet his grandad and go for a drink. He didn't drink too much. He was a professional athlete, and he liked to spend time with Pop who was still singing strongly in his 80s. When he was free he would nip down for a swift half on a Wednesday evening, after choir practice was over.

He enjoyed being a local celebrity. Certainly he didn't enjoy national fame like some other sportsmen of lesser ability in higher profile sports.

Rugby league was often ignored by the national media. That didn't stop him being a local celebrity, however and he liked walking into situations like the choir and being recognised by everyone. Fifty faces smiled and nodded as if he were smiling at each one of them individually. When he went to the pub with his Pop, everyone knew him. People would stop and have a word. This was real fame, not the fame of a footballer who drives away in his flash car after a game to a distant, hidden place guarded by security cameras. In his sport he was part of the community. He was involved and valued that involvement.

He wasn't a fool however. He was well paid for his talent. £70,000 a year was not a lot compared to footballers, but the alternative for most local players when he started out had been mining and it was a lot better than that.

He had had a very successful playing career. In 2004 he had won a Challenge Cup winners medal in front of 70,000 people. Castleton had beaten Wigan 16–8 in one of the biggest cup final shocks of all time. He had won the man-of-the-match award and the trophy, together with the medal, took pride of place in a display cabinet.

Unfortunately, two things had eluded him. Castleton was a small town of 70,000 people. Its rugby team lacked the resources to be among the very top clubs. They were a small town club that had achieved wonders with their limited resources. They had never won the league championship; their best position had been third place in 1999. The team was a good one, but as soon as first choice players became injured there weren't enough replacements of a similar quality waiting to step in. Often good players played half the season carrying an injury that should have had sidelined them for treatment, but they played on. When even the most talented players are only performing at 90 per cent, they lose games and these problems limited Castleton's achievements.

Other players, anxious to realise rewards they felt their talents deserved, had moved on to bigger clubs. Chris understood their reasons. They had families to support and wanted to achieve the maximum in both financial and playing terms. He had seen players that he had played with as a boy go on to earn double what he was being paid. Some had won international honours which was something that still eluded him. Some expert commentators had said that he was the best second-row forward never to play for Great Britain. Now he had decided that, at the age of 31, he had lost his chance.

He often wondered what would have happened if he had moved on. His wife Caroline had wanted him to, but he just couldn't seem to do it. Three years ago he almost signed for Leeds. He agonised over it for weeks and then just as he was almost convinced that it was the right thing to do, his dad, the man who had trained him in his earliest years, who Chris thought was responsible for his later progress, died suddenly. He withdrew from the negotiations and the opportunity passed. He had no regrets, or so he thought.

Then, without warning, Caroline had left him. Things had not been going well for a long time. Looking back, Chris could see that she had felt frustrated by his apparent lack of ambition. Perhaps his refusal to sign for Leeds was the final straw. A month after his dad's funeral she left him. A note was waiting for him when he got home from a training session. She had met someone else and that was that. He sat there stunned in disbelief, reading the words again and again. She said he was self-centred, more in love with rugby than her.

As a result he'd lived by himself for the last three years. They had divorced and he had not contested it. At least he still saw his daughters. To be truthful he was pleased the rows had stopped. He hated being shouted at. He'd put it down to her, but now he saw that maybe he'd had some say in it. Maybe she was right. Maybe he did care more about rugby than her. Maybe it was for the best.

For now he was concentrating on playing and the future. He had it all planned. He had three seasons left as a player, maybe only two, and he wanted to make the most of those years first. When he retired he would start coaching. He had already passed the first of the national coaching certificates and was helping the main amateur team in the area. Things were going well. They had won promotion in his

51

first season and were doing well in the top division. The next step would be as an assistant coach to a full-time side before taking over as the senior coach of a lower, semi-professional club. Then after another two years he would apply for senior coaching positions in the top flight. After that who knew? He hoped to coach the national team, but that was a long way off. He had to keep his feet on the ground.

All in all, life was good. He was lucky. Maybe Caroline had been right. He certainly didn't miss her. Yes, he was very lucky. As he took a seat at the back of the room he saw Karl, the kid in the wheelchair, coming out to get his coat. He came down the side of the choir and turned to face the front. They smiled at each other and watched as Carol put his coat on him.

Yes he was certainly lucky. He had two wonderful daughters. He enjoyed his career and he knew what his future was going to be. He had much to be grateful for, not like that poor sod.

The choir finished its rehearsal with a rousing rendition of a song he'd never heard of. It wasn't his kind of music, but it was certainly a very impressive sound and he was proud of his grandad. He was a doer. He'd been a good amateur player in his youth and had worked hard down the mines to provide for his family. At 83 Pop was still tall and lean. He was always smartly dressed and possessed a winning smile and a bad cough, although he never seemed to cough when he sang. Singing seemed to do his chest good. The choir was full of elderly men who looked younger than they were. Singing seemed to keep them alive. It kept them fit and interested. They had something to learn, something to practice and something to get dressed up for.

It had certainly helped when grandma died. The whole choir had been very kind. Twenty of them had sung at her funeral. She had always supported the choir and they turned out for her. It had been very touching.

Now, at the end of rehearsal, they were going for a pint. Chris always liked the way his grandad jumped into activity when he arrived. They were always pleased to see each other.

Pop waved goodbye with his hat. They walked out of the main hall and stepped into the darkness. George gave out a little grunt as the cold air hit him before he could fasten his coat.

"Bit nippy!"

"Aye."

"You get a bit warm singing for two hours."

"I'll bet you do."

The two men walked to Chris's car. Five minutes later they were entering into the bar of their local, The Green Dragon.

John thanked Carol as she held open the door. They were always the last to leave. Karl was unable to do much for himself and could not help them much as they struggled to put his coat on.

Then they would reverse the process they had carried out when they arrived. John checked the handbrake before opening the back door. After fitting the ramps and checking their alignment, he cast one quick look at the brake before Karl pushed the lever forward. The chair slowly rose and John's hand again rested on the back, 'just in case'. John clambered in, fitted the straps and checked that Karl was comfy.

Carol then left. "Bye Karl. See you next week."

"Maybe."

"What do you mean maybe? You're always there."

"Well if I'm not too tired."

"Oh, okay love, bye then."

Carol and John exchanged glances. Karl was thinking about not coming? Life was becoming littered with knowing glances.

It was obvious that Karl was getting more tired each week. John had been wondering how many more times he could manage to stay for the whole evening. Now perhaps he was about to find out. He decided to say nothing. He'd let Karl decide. Maybe he would feel differently next week.

"I'll see you next week John."

"Oh aye, I'll be there even if this lazy sod isn't."

They smiled, but Karl did not bite.

He indicated right as they exited the main drive that led from the church hall. They went over the same speed bumps and Karl grunted just as he had done on the earlier journey in. The trip home was always quieter, but despite his fatigue, he suddenly became very animated.

"Did you ask him?"

"Ask who?" he teased.

"The man."

"What man?"

"Mr Anderton."

"Mr Anderton?"

"Yes. You know. Chris Anderton's grandad.

"Oh you mean George?"

"Yes. Did you ask him?"

"Ask him what?"

"If he'd do my social?"

"What social?"

"My social for my bloody chair!"

"Oh you mean your social?"

"Yes."

"No."

"What?"

"Sorry mate, completely slipped my mind. We'll have to wait until next week."

Karl said nothing for the rest of the journey. John was dying to tell him, but he loved to tease him.

Ten minutes later they came to a halt outside Sarah's house. She was stood on the front step waiting as she always did and waved as she came down the path to meet them.

He applied the handbrake.

He couldn't see her face properly, but there was a weariness in her walk. 'You need to get out of the house more', he thought to himself. He had said as much to her several times, but she had never done so. She could go out when he took Karl to choir. He could put him to bed. It was no problem, but she was unable to place a burden on her parents, no matter how many times they offered. Sometimes it seemed as if she didn't want to or was unable to enjoy herself. It had been years since her husband had died, but she had not moved on. He knew she had a lot on, but even so, she had to have some time to herself, some fun.

He smiled at his daughter as he got out and checked the handbrake once more before taking a now sleepy Karl out of the back. They moved slowly towards the front door as John packed things away and locked up. He followed them in just to check that everything was ok, staying just long enough to say what he had to say.

As he went to leave he turned in the doorway.

"Oh, by the way..."

Karl stopped in the hall. The back of his head listened.

"He's going to ask him, tonight."

"Honest?"

"Honest."

"I knew. You old bugger!"

"Eh, less of the old."

He winked at his daughter.

"Do you need anything?"

"No thanks dad, I can cope."

"Right then. Night, night."

He paused.

"If you do need anything?"

"I know where you are."

They smiled at one another. John shut the door behind him. He was tired as well as his grandson. He would never say anything to Sarah, but looking after Karl did take it out of him. He didn't mind of course, but his weariness only confirmed his earlier thoughts about his daughter. If he was tired, how exhausted was she? He left the car outside Sarah's and went home to his wife.

By 10.30pm an excited Karl had had enough, as had his mother. Wednesdays always meant a late night and Karl had begun to find Thursday mornings difficult. Sarah wanted to keep things as normal as

54

she could for as long as she could, but she knew it was getting harder for him. She was not aware of what Karl had said earlier.

There was another reason why her son had to be in bed increasingly early. She needed her rest as well. Karl had to be turned every hour to avoid bed sores. She had not had a continuous night's sleep for two years. It was she, more than anyone, who needed an early night.

Ten minutes after they had left the choir, Chris and George had taken off their overcoats, parked them on a stool and were taking the first sips of bitter.

"Aye that's grand. Just what my throat needed after two hours singing."

"How long do you sing for Pop?"

"Two hours, why?"

"Nothing."

"Are you taking the piss?"

Chris laughed.

"Me, no Pop."

There was a pause.

"Two hours then?"

"All right, so I might have mentioned it once or twice."

"Once or twice?! It's every bloody week!"

"Well so what. It's hard work singing for..."

"How long?"

"I'm not talking."

Chris loved being with his grandad. They were best mates as well as relatives. There was a natural warmth between them that dismissed the years. They talked about everything, the choir, training, the team, his dad. They always paused after talking about him. One man had lost a son, the other his father. Perhaps the silence was a mark of respect or just an unspoken agreement to take stock of something about him.

"I've got a request for you."

"Oh aye?"

"You can say no if you want."

"I will."

"John Black, one of the choir, you know the big fellah with white hair and glasses?"

"Aye."

"Well they're raising funds for his grandson to get him a new electric wheelchair."

"Karl?"

"Aye."

"Isn't he entitled to one?"

"I don't know the details. Anyway he needs a new electric one, better than standard issue I suppose. The kid can't walk and he's certainly not strong enough to push himself. Anyway, to cut a long story short he asked me if you'd make an appearance at a fundraising night."

"Yeah, sure. When?"

"I don't know. It's not been arranged yet. I just said I'd ask in principle. I knew you'd say 'yes', but I said I'd have a word."

"Just tell him to let me know."

"You can tell him yourself."

"When?"

"After training on Monday. He goes to watch with Karl during the school holidays."

"Of course, that's where I've seen him. It didn't click. I see them quite often. Oh I'll see him next Monday."

"So you'll do it?"

"Of course. You know I'll be only too pleased. No problem."

"That's what I told him. Aye."

"Aye."

"Aye."

"Aye".

"Are you taking the piss again?"

"Me Pop? Whatever gave you that idea?"

11. I can speak!

As it happened Chris didn't train on Monday. He had played on Sunday in a rearranged fixture, so Monday was a rest day. On Tuesday training finished at 3pm.

Chris finished his session and was walking off the pitch towards the shower room. The training pitch was at the front of the ground. An eight foot wall fronted on to the main road which passed the front entrance. At each end of the wall stood two sets of huge gates which opened onto cinder covered drives where spectators streamed in on match days. On training days, the players' cars were parked along the right-hand drive.

Both these drives took spectators to banks of turnstiles by which they entered the ground. In between these banks stood the shop that sold shirts, mugs, diaries, track suits and more. All the paint-work was in red and white, the team's colours. Overhead a large sign that lit up on match days simply said "Welcome to Castleton".

Castleton RLFC had resisted having one of the nicknames that other teams had adopted when rugby league became a full-time professional sport. Their traditional name was enough.

At the side of the shop was a red door. Written on it were the words 'Player's entrance'. Chris was heading towards this door and the pleasure of a warm shower. Training in the depths of late winter could be very unpleasant and although it was a pleasant sunny day in mid February, it was still very cold. He was about to open the door when he noticed a man, out of the corner of his eye, moving towards him. He knew him from somewhere and just as it dawned on him that it was Karl's grandad from the choir.

"Chris?"

"Yes."

"I'm John Black from the choir."

"Yes, I know. Pop spoke to me about Karl."

Chris nodded over John's shoulder to the figure in a wheelchair who had crept up behind.

"Hallo Karl".

Karl smiled shyly.

"I didn't realise it was you two. You often come to training don't you?"

"Yes," replied Karl excitedly. "We come most weeks when I'm not at school, unless I'm poorly."

"I just didn't link you with the choir," smiled Chris.

"Funny how you put people in pigeon holes."

"Aye. Don't you get cold sat out here?"

"Sometimes, aye. Thermal underwear's marvellous isn't it? He won't miss it. He keeps an eye on everything. He knows how all the players are doing and what their strengths and weaknesses are. He's a proper encyclopaedia."

They smiled, the grandfather hopeful, the boy worshipful and the player doing a routine community liaison job.

"George spoke to you about Karl?"

"Aye, he did." It was strange, but even at the age of 31 he still found it awkward when people referred to his grandfather as George. Everyone in the family called him Pop. Even Chris's grandmother had called him Pop.

"No problem."

"You'll do it?"

"Of course. It would be a pleasure."

Chris meant it, it would be a pleasure. Professional rugby league players are required to do a certain amount of community work to help build up the club's following and to set a good example to young people. Chris enjoyed it. He was a part of the community and liked putting something back.

"If you go into the office and ask for Claire, she'll make the arrangements with you and I'll turn up. It's as simple as that. Okay?"

"Yes fine, thanks."

The boy and the old man beamed at each other and then, in unison turned and beamed at Chris.

"Does Karl want my autograph?" Chris whispered to John.

"I'm here. You can ask me. I'm here"

Chris immediately recognised his mistake. They been told about it when they did community liaison training. It was called 'does he take sugar?' and referred to dealing with disabled people as if they couldn't speak for themselves. Chris had made a gaffe.

"Sorry."

"I can speak for myself, you know."

"I'm sure you can."

Chris smiled. Karl did not. The boy had told him a simple truth.

"Anyway, I've got your autograph. I've got the whole team. I got it last year at the cup final."

"Oh yes. I remember now."

There was a pause.

"I'll see you later."

They shook hands. As he went to the shower room Chris thought to himself, 'that kid can stick up for himself'.

He did not know yet that 'that kid' could do more than stick up for himself. Chris's life was never going to be the same.

12. An education

The new season was now in full swing. Rugby league had become a full-time professional sport at the top level a few years before. Linked with this change was a shift of season to being a summer sport. In practice this had meant that the season began at the end of February and finished in October with a Grand Final to decide who were to become the champions. Although much of the winter was avoided, it still meant that much of the season involved the cold and wet, particularly if a test series against Australia or New Zealand was played in November.

Karl's social event was to be held on Saturday 30 April. This was fortunate because most games were played on Sunday afternoons although some were on Friday or Saturday nights to suit the television broadcasters who put so much money into the sport.

Saturday was ideal. It meant that Chris would have no problems attending. He could show up, do the necessary smiling and handshaking, pose for a few photographs and then go home. Normally he didn't go out on a Saturday when he was playing the following day. He would go to bed early to ensure a good night's sleep. He would not drink alcohol the night before a match. In fact he hardly touched it anyway. Supporters were only too willing to criticise a bad performance and he did not want to fuel rumours by being seen to be out on the town. He valued his performances and his image. This was different, however. It was part of his community liaison role and had been approved by the club. He would also be seen by loyal fans to be drinking fruit juice.

He was required to be at the Ruskin Lane club house for 8pm. He always arrived early. It was simply good manners and professional. An early appearance meant that the organisers didn't have to worry about whether the 'star' would turn up. Chris took pride in his professionalism. He cared about his fans. After all they paid his wages. They were important.

He parked and walked across to the social club, a pleasant single storey building covered in ivy. Chris loved this time of year. The days were getting longer. Spring flowers were out everywhere and, well, he just liked this time of year.

He found the 'Yorkshire Suite and went in. Three people stood at the bar. They nodded. Chris nodded back. A series of tables lined the edge of the room, leaving the dance floor free. In the far corner a disc jockey was busily setting up his equipment. Chris did not see anyone he recognised. One of the three men came across from the bar.

"Now then young man, I'm John's brother Malcolm. Karl will be here with his mother and grandad shortly."

They shook hands. It would be an evening of shaking hands.

"Can I buy you a drink?"

"Lemonade please."

John's brother smiled.

"Of course. Got to be in top shape eh? As I said Karl will be here in a few minutes. Good game last week eh?"

Chris's mouth opened, but the collision of wheelchair against wood tore the reply from him as Karl forced his way through the double doors.

"Now that's what I call an entrance," shouted Malcolm.

Karl beamed as he saw the room. He entered like royalty. Immediately behind him were his entourage who Chris presumed were members of his family. There was a sister who looked older and an obviously younger brother, his grandfather John and what he presumed must be his mother and grandmother.

The mother was good looking, slim and about five foot two. She was not as he had expected, although if he had been asked, he wouldn't have known what he expected, except it wasn't this. She smiled and fussed round her son, but there was something else. He'd noticed it immediately. She was tired. He felt it more than he saw it. Her good looks were not betrayed by lines or wrinkles. He couldn't explain it. It was just something that hit him the moment she walked into the room. This woman had a lot of cares and woes.

John came across guiding her towards him. She smiled as they shook hands and Chris wondered where her husband was.

"Chris. This is my daughter, Sarah, Karl's mum."

He also noticed sadness. What was he, a psychic? He had never noticed such things in people before, but this woman's difficulties smacked him right in the face.

"Hello. Thank you for coming. Karl is always talking about you."

Chris smiled. He liked the hero worship, but it nevertheless left him a little embarrassed.

"He's got good taste."

They smiled.

"He's got your picture on the wall."

"I'm honoured."

They smiled.

"Do you watch rugby with Karl?"

"Only rarely now. He goes with his grandad. It's good for them. I used to go".

She stopped in mid-sentence and looked into the distance. He could see sadness once more.

"I suppose it gives you a bit of a break?"

She came back.

"Yes. I get the house cleaned! That's my break."

"It must be very difficult."

"Sometimes."

Suddenly realising that talking about her difficulties on a rare night out was probably the last thing that she needed, he changed the subject.

"What would you like me to do?"

The public relations people at the club had already briefed Chris about what was required, but it was a good way to make conversation. He was good at getting people to talk and it broke the ice. Often people wanted a celebrity to attend some function or other, but hadn't a clue what to do when they arrived. He was good at making idle conversation and putting people at their ease. During the evening he shook hands and greeted people. He had dozens of conversations about the same things; the team's prospects, the qualities of different players, the inside story on big games he had played in.

It was the same thing at every public function. He had the same conversations every time. It was par for the course. He had got quite skilled at smiling. The real trick was not to let the clients see a hint of boredom. It had to look and sound like the most interesting chat he had ever had. Normally he could deal with these events routinely, but he was struck by the intensity of the evening. Everyone seemed to want it to go so well. Finally at nine o'clock a loud cheer went up when Chris was brought on stage to wave to the guests. He drew the raffle and then was asked to announce that the evening had raised £542.

Chris returned to the bar and ordered a fruit juice. He would be leaving soon because he wanted an early night, but decided that it would be a good idea to talk to Karl for a few minutes. After shaking his hand gently Chris was given a chair next to him.

"We've done well, haven't we?"

Karl nodded. Chris was used to doing all the talking with star struck fans who couldn't think what to say.

"Your long spin pass to the right needs to improve."

Chris was taken aback.

"Does it?" he said meekly.

"Yes. The coaching of British players is not as detailed as Australians. That's why they are better than us. Don't you remember the Bradford coach, you know that Australian, saying that he had to teach professional players things they would teach 16 year olds in Australia? Things get missed. Has nobody ever told you?"

Chris had almost forgotten what the original point was.

"Er, no."

When you try to do a long pass on your weaker side you swing your shoulders like a throw across your body."

"Do I?"

"Yes, what it means is that your pass curves behind the player you're aiming at and he has to stop to catch the ball. That slows his momentum down."

"Really? How do you know this?"

"Because I watch you. You're an excellent player, but you could get better."

"Right."

Chris didn't know whether to thank this kid or just politely ignore his advice. Karl continued: "If you strengthen your wrists and use them more and keep your shoulders straight the pass will be straighter and faster. It will open up defences with the increased speed of the pass and the player you're aiming at will run on to the ball faster."

"How do you know all this? You've never..."

"I can't play the game so I study it. I've read all the coaching manuals and I listen to commentators and coaches. You pick up things."

"I can see that."

"Most players don't even know all the rules, let alone techniques and coaching. They just play and often they just carry on with bad habits. Most players don't know why they are good. They just are. They don't study the game. I read. There's a bloke in America who coaches American Football players to kick better. He's in a wheelchair. He's never kicked a ball in his life, but he's studied sports science. He can show players on a computer about body angles and stuff. He can show them how to improve. Everyone can improve."

"So what do I need to do?"

Chris could not believe he was taking notice of this kid. True, he was a captive audience and it would have been impossible to walk away from the very person he was supposed to be helping, but it was more than that. Maybe the kid had a point. Maybe he was right. He certainly made sense and so they chatted. They spoke for another hour without a break. It was an education for Chris and a dream come true for Karl.

Across the room Sarah sat watching. She was happy. She had not seen Karl look so alive in months. He was beaming and she was impressed with the rugby player. He was kind and paid attention to her son. He took what he had to say seriously when he didn't need to.

"He's rather nice, isn't he?"

Her mother's voice strained to make itself heard over the music.

"Yes he is. He talks nicely to Karl."

"I didn't mean that. I've been watching you. You've not taken your eyes off him."

"What? Don't be daft. I've been looking after Karl."

"Don't you think it's time you looked after yourself a bit?"

"What do you mean?"

"Have a bit of fun?"

"I'm fine mum, honestly."

Mum smiled.

"Okay, but he is nice."

Sarah smiled, but the smile concealed her true emotions. She did think Chris was attractive. Seeing him close-up had only confirmed what she had thought beforehand and she liked the way he spoke to her son. She wanted to dismiss the idea her mother had suggested, but maybe the suggestion itself, by her mother of all people, had given her permission to think about it. Something else dawned on her as she sat there in the corner. She was smiling. Then she stopped. What was she smiling about anyway? It wasn't practical. She didn't even know if he was married or not. Even if he was single, men didn't take on women with three kids, let alone one with a severely disabled child. Anyway, he hadn't even asked her and she wasn't going to ask him.

"Would you like to dance?"

"What?"

He was standing in front of her.

"Your son has given me permission to ask you for a dance."

He smiled.

She tried to think of a reason not to, but he was already leading her to the dance floor. Three dances later they were walking off together towards Karl.

"Right, it's time to take you home young man" said Sarah.

"He's a bright lad" said Chris.

"Oh he's bright alright. He's a world authority on rugby league."

"I can see".

"Aye."

Sarah turned to him: "I can't thank you enough."

"It was my pleasure."

They shook hands and then said brief goodbyes. She disappeared like Cinderella running from the ball. Karl steered his wheelchair into the car park. From the padding that supported his head he shouted "Remember what I said. If you do what I say you'll be an international this year." With that they were gone.

As they pulled out of the grounds and into the main road June turned to her daughter and said "Told you he was nice," and turned back without waiting for a reply.

Nothing more was said about it, but all the way back home Karl couldn't help asking himself a question over and over again: 'Does mum fancy Chris?'

Chris strolled back to his car and left. Before he knew it he was home. He'd driven on automatic pilot while his brain had dealt with everything the boy had said. In his whole career nobody had educated him like he had. The boy seemed to know everything. He sat on the sofa and drank a slow bottle of beer. One wouldn't do any harm and he sat there, thinking in the silence. The need for an early night seemed less important than before. A kid in a wheelchair had stunned him into silence. The kid knew more than he did. He thought about the game more than he did. The kid was right. Most players, including him, just play. He realised that, even in this latter part of his career, he could improve his game. He laughed and said a toast to Karl and thought about his mother. All in all it had been a good night.

13. The visit

Sarah was dreaming. She was lying on her ledge in silence. For some reason, she stirred. She had not moved since she was placed there until now. Swinging her legs round she sat up and was surprised, as the darkness became light. To her astonishment she was not sitting on a ledge at all, but on a rock by a babbling brook that ran sharply down the hillside. She put her hand in the cool, refreshing water and listened to its music played to an accompaniment of birds singing in the trees that surrounded her. Sunlight danced through the glade and played with the branches and leaves. It was warm and soothing. Unlike her previous times there, she felt safe in her dream. She could stay here forever. Then, after a minute of enchantment she saw the figure of a man standing at the brow of the hill. He was watching her and smiling. It was Dave. Sarah waved and he waved back. She shouted to him and started to climb upwards, but he did not answer her. She climbed and climbed, but did not get any closer.

Stumbling over rocks, she looked down to check her footing. When she looked up she found herself at the top. She could see for miles, but there was no sign of him. Standing there alone, Sarah realised that it was an illusion. She fell to her knees and sobbed, only to find that she had returned to her ledge and the silence.

It was approaching Christmas. Karl had started college in September. The four of them sat round the dining table finishing their tea. Sarah always insisted on the evening meal being eaten together. She was simply not going to allow family life to disintegrate. As John and Mel finished off their last fish fingers Sarah offered the last mouthful of food to Karl who took it like some overgrown chick impatient for its parent's last offering.

"Listen. It's Christmas in a month. I haven't heard you ask for anything yet."

All three kids sat silently. They all knew that their mum had no spare cash. Their best presents always came from their grandparents. They tried not to ask while always hoping for the best.

"Well?"

"Some make up will do me fine mum. That would be nice."

"Could I have a CD?" asked James.

She turned to Karl.

"The *Rugby League Annual Review.*"

"Now there's a surprise."

It was James's turn to dry while Mel cleared the table and wiped it. The home ran like clockwork. It was the only way to cope with Karl's increasing dependency.

As they sat down again to drink a cup of tea before the kids retreated to their rooms, Karl asked a question that surprised Sarah.

"Mum?"

"Yes."

"Do you think we could get Chris Anderton to come to the Christmas party at college?

"I don't know."

"Only you did say we'd see him again."

"Did I? When?"

"At the social when he came."

Karl's new chair had been delivered just a fortnight before. It was a great improvement. It was bigger and stronger than the last one and yet at the same time more manoeuvrable. It also had a large curved headrest that could hold his head in position. The chair had maintained his mobility while his physical condition continued to deteriorate. Every time Sarah looked at the chair she felt gratitude to everyone who had helped raise money towards it. She didn't like to impose on people and yet she couldn't deny that she enjoyed the thought of meeting Chris again. He reminded her of Dave in many ways. He was quietly spoken and thoughtful with a strong athletic figure and a mop of black hair. She smiled.

"Mum? Did you hear what I said?"

"Er, yes. I, er, don't know. It's such short notice."

"Well couldn't you try? That would be my best Christmas present."

Sarah's eyes flashed at him.

"Do I detect a hint of manipulation here?"

Karl smiled. She knew what he was doing and what's more Karl knew that she knew. They smiled at each other.

"Mum fancies him."

"I do not."

"Oh that was a bit sharp," teased Mel.

"I don't fancy him."

"Well, everyone else does."

"That doesn't mean I do."

"Okay." Mel carried on with the dishes. She whispered something to John and they both giggled.

"What?"

"Er, nothing," they both chimed, leaving no doubt that there was something.

"Look will you ask him or not?"

Sarah turned quickly from Mel's comments back to Karl. She was trapped and she knew it. She refused Karl nothing that she could afford and this request would involve no cost.

"I'll try."

The kids went to their rooms. Mel was going out to see her boyfriend and James wanted to watch television. She went with Karl to switch on his computer. Every evening he would play games on it or surf the internet for an hour before going to bed. He was getting tired easily now and was often in bed by nine, sometimes eight o clock. She left him to his games and returned to the front room. She turned the television on and flicked from one channel to the next. There was nothing worth watching, so she turned it off. Sarah hated this time of day. Sometimes she would read, but she was often too tired and simply needed something to occupy her on the screen until Karl was ready for a wash and bed.

Caring for a child with Karl's level of dependency didn't leave room for much of a social life. She didn't have time for socialising and even if she did, she didn't have the money. Mel and the lads often told her to go out, but she rarely did. She always felt so tired and perhaps, if she was able to admit it, there was a hint of fear. Were the kids and her mother right? Was she hiding herself away? She could see Dave's face. She always smiled at him before tears trickled down her face. She tried to convince herself that she had so much to be grateful for, a nice home, wonderful kids, helpful parents, but there was no disguising Dave's absence. She sighed.

As she lay back on the sofa in silence she could hear the music coming from James's room. She smiled at the thought of the conversation at tea time.

The truth was that Mel had touched a nerve. She did like Chris, but she always told herself that she never had the time to think about such things. If she was honest it was deeper than that. She felt guilty. She couldn't imagine, had never imagined, herself with anyone else.

Anyway the idea was silly. She didn't even know if he was involved with anyone. No, the thought of a relationship was impossible. She smiled at Dave's image once more. Regardless of what she felt or thought, she knew that her son's wishes would be complied with and she would have to talk to Chris sooner rather than later.

The telephone rang and rang. Although Sarah did not want to admit it she was nervous. Three days had passed since Karl had asked her. Each day as he left, he had turned to her imploringly,

"You won't forget, will you?"

"No, I promise."

Each evening she had felt guilty when his hopeful expression disappeared as he got off the bus.

"He wasn't in. I'm ringing tomorrow," had been the first excuse. It had been followed by "I phoned and they said I'd just missed him. I've left a message."

She was running out of lies.

She didn't know why her heart was in her mouth. She knew that in phoning the main office she would not be talking to Chris. It would probably be some young girl on a training scheme. They would then take a message and say that Chris was unavailable, probably training or out on some community liaison work. So why was she nervous?

The phone carried on ringing as Sarah sat there, her head propped up by her left hand as it held the receiver. The fingers of her right hand drummed continuously on the table until she began to annoy herself.

She was just about to put the phone down when a voice answered.

"Hello, Castleton Rugby League Football Club." It was a man's voice.

"Er hello. I wanted to talk to the lady who organises visits by players."

"They're all busy at the moment. Can I help?"

"Well I was phoning to see whether I could arrange for Chris Anderton to give out some Christmas presents at my son's college party?"

"Well we don't normally do routine party visits. There are so many."

"Which college is it?"

"Well it's the special needs department at Helen Keller College. Chris has helped us before."

"Is that Karl's mum?"

Sarah was taken aback.

"Er, yes."

"Hello. It's Chris."

"Oh... right."

There was a pause. Sarah nervously wrapped the chord around her finger.

"What are you doing answering the phone?"

He laughed. "Well even top mega stars like me use phones you know."

"Yes, of course. I just didn't think that you'd be answering it in the office."

"I just happened to be in the office and they're busy. When is it?"

"The party?"

"No, the day trip to the moon."

She was surprised at how friendly he was.

"Well?"

"Er it's on Friday the 17th, the day they break up."

"What time?"

"10.30. AM that is".

"Well I didn't think it would be pm." He laughed.

She smiled. He had a nice easy manner, just like Dave. Then she stopped smiling when she thought of her husband.

"How many people will be there?"

"Oh it's only small. There are about 20 kids and their helpers. It's very friendly."

"Has he settled in all right at college? I know he said he was a bit nervous about going."

"When did he say that?"

"He mentioned it one day when he saw me at training."

"Oh."

Sarah was a little shocked he knew something about her son that she didn't. There was another pause.

"Yep, I can do that. No problem."

" Oh, er right. You'll need directions."

"No problem, give us your number and I'll ring you the day before."

"Right then, lovely."

"I'll wait to hear from you."

"No problem. Bye."

"Bye."

She put the phone down. Karl would be chuffed to bits and what's more Chris had her phone number. It would be fine. No problem.

Chris always took his public duties very seriously. In all his time at the club he had never been late or let anyone down apart from one occasion when he broke his ankle the day before he was due to make an appearance. Then his apologies had been made for him by the club office and they had sent another player in his stead. It had been a Christmas Eve visit to the children's ward of a local hospital. One little girl had evidently been very upset because she would not be meeting her favourite player and it was reported in the local press about her spoilt Christmas.

The following week's paper showed a delighted fan receiving a home visit from Chris. The child had suffered a broken pelvis in a car accident and the paper described how they had swapped stories about broken bones and pain and getting mum to do everything for you.

Chris smiled as he recalled her giggles. Still smiling, he swung the car into the narrow drive that led to Helen Keller College. As he did so, a youth on a pushbike appeared from nowhere. He braked suddenly as the youth went past him. Riding against the one-way system the young man stuck his middle finger in the air in Chris's direction. Chris watched the young man's progress down the drive and out of the car park. He parked, got out of the car and straightened his suit.

Unlike his younger colleagues he always wore a suit on these occasions instead of a tracksuit. He liked to look smart and felt that a suit indicated the importance of what he was doing. He walked towards reception and hesitated slightly, surprised as the automatic doors opened and invited him in to a blue reception area that was obviously a new addition to an old building. He registered as a visitor.

Deborah phoned the special needs department to inform them of their guest's arrival and motioned him to sit down. He was just at the point of no return in his descent when Sarah came through the wooden doors. He tried to stop sitting down, but couldn't. Instead he comically fell into the seat before scrambling back up in an undignified manner accompanied by a "whoops". They both laughed and shook hands. He liked her laugh, he thought, before he offered her the flowers held in his hand.

"Oh, for me?"

"Well I just thought mum should get something seeing as her son will get all the attention."

"Oh, he always makes certain he gets the attention. Thank you."

"No problem."

She laughed. He always said "No problem," in a flat monotone. There was something amusing about the way he said it. He sounded a little, well, gormless.

"What are you laughing at?"

"Nothing." She recovered quickly. "Thank you, it was a lovely thought."

"I didn't know you actually worked here."

"I don't. I just help out sometimes as a volunteer and come for special occasions as well. Do you want to come through?"

They walked into a corridor that passed through the refectory. It was heaving with young people and music blasted out from two wall-mounted television screens fixed diagonally opposite each other. Just as soon as they had entered, they left it again passing through another set of wooden doors that were controlled by a large button which said 'Push to open'. Leaving the noise behind they passed beneath a sign that said 'Learning Support'. They approached yet another set of doors. This time the door opened by itself and a young woman whizzed past them in an electric wheelchair, travelling at some speed. She laughed as Chris stepped nimbly out of the way.

"Jess, be careful."

A member of staff passed by in pursuit.

"Sorry she's excited and she needs the toilet. Hello, see you later."

With that she followed in the same direction towards the toilets signposted for disabled access.

He entered the room and was surprised by the scene that greeted him. A CD player blasted out from a table at the back. The tables were covered by tablecloths and plates of food. Balloons and decorations hung from every corner and above the door to an office. Young people, some in wheelchairs, others not, crowded into this room. It was noisy, alive and, Chris noted, happy. Sarah guided him towards

70

the office door. He smiled in greeting to everyone in turn. A woman in a bright yellow jumper with matching nails and wearing a Christmas hat was sat at a desk speaking on the telephone.

Sarah shut the door and the noise levels reduced. He sat down.

"Yes his bus leaves at 1.30 pm today. I know it's normally 3.30 but the college is closing at 1.30pm. We informed transport of the time changes over a fortnight ago."

"Right... Right... Right, okay then. So the bus will definitely be here? Thank goodness for that. Okay love. No... Thanks. Yes and merry Christmas to you to. Bye".

The yellow person turned and smiled at Chris.

"Hi, I'm Julie. It's so nice of you to come."

"No problem."

He felt that Sarah was smiling to herself again.

"Would you like a drink of anything, tea coffee, lemonade?"

"Coke" piped up another voice as a young woman came in.

"This is Sue."

They nodded at each other.

"Poor chap. There's that many names flying at you, you won't remember them all."

Chris smiled.

"I'd like lemonade please."

"Has Sarah told you what's happening?"

"Well, you just want me to give out a few presents?"

"Yes. It's nothing fancy. There's presents under the tree that the kids have got each other. It's an excuse for those who follow rugby to talk to you really."

"And an excuse to keep 'em under control."

This was yet another voice that had appeared from nowhere.

"This is Neil. He's the only man in the department."

"Oh, thanks Julie".

Chris smiled. Chris often felt uncomfortable when he first arrived at a place where he was the guest of honour, but he had soon been made to feel at ease.

He was impressed at how lively and happy the students were. These people obviously did a thoroughly good job.

There was a knock at the door. Neil opened it.

"Yes Michelle?"

A short plump girl with brown hair bounced into the room.

"When's this rugby man coming?

"You mean?"

"Yes, that good looking one."

"You mean me?"

"Not you. You're not good looking."

"Oh thanks Michelle. He's there."

71

"Where?"

"There".

With that Michelle faced Chris and said "Hiya".

Without saying another word and grinning from ear to ear she left as quickly and as bouncily as she had entered. Chris was nonplussed.

"Is she always like that?"

"Yep" said four voices in unison.

"She's one of the brighter ones."

Chris smiled. He had forgotten all about the youth who had sped past on a bike as he was driving into the car park when suddenly the door burst open and he was standing there.

"Here you are Julie. I got 'em."

"Oh thanks James you are a good lad. We'd have had no music without these."

She took a handful of CDs off the young man who stood there grinning. "Do you want to take them and start playing them? The one we've got will be finished soon."

"Oh yeah, great. Can I be the DJ?"

Julie nodded and the youth left to perform his duties without paying Chris the slightest attention.

"He's a good lad." Julie said, smiling.

No brains but a heart of gold. He cycled home to get some CDs because I'd forgotten to bring mine in. What a good lad."

Chris smiled and told them about the incident in the car park.

"Oh dear," said Julie. I'll have a word with him."

Chris decided not to pursue it and sat there smiling as Sue handed him his lemonade.

"Just because they're labelled 'Special Needs' it doesn't make them angels," she added.

"Is it always this busy?" He asked.

"It's bedlam." Julie replied. "The college doesn't stop. We have a special needs section which is geared to, well, people who have a learning or physical disability."

"And what do you do?"

"Look after them. We write for the physically disabled, feed them, toilet them as needed. Some need more help than others. Some are quite independent. Others need help with everything."

"Do they have special lessons?"

"Some do. Others do all kind of courses. It depends. People often think that being 'special needs' means being thick. It's not true. We have students with learning difficulties and others with physical problems. Some of our students are really clever. They just need a fair chance."

Bright posters covered the wall along with dozens of photographs. They showed the teachers and student aides sitting with former and current students. It was a record of the life of this room. People who had come and gone. Fading images of young kids whose lives had been touched by these people.

"Are these all yours?"

Sue pointed to the pictures. "Rob's at university studying computers. He was a fantastic lad. He couldn't walk. He couldn't feed himself. He couldn't toilet himself, yet he typed all his notes out using a head pointer. You know? A metal pointer strapped to his head? In the four years he was here, he never handed in his homework late".

"What was up with him?"

"We try not to say that something was 'up' with anyone."

"Oh, I'm sorry."

"What needs did he have?"

Sue smiled at his attempt to use the right terms.

"Ooh, not bad! Rob had cerebral palsy. It's caused by a lack of oxygen at birth."

"So he had to use a wheelchair?"

"Cerebral palsy can affect people in different ways. They don't all need a chair by any means."

Chris looked at another picture. It showed a very thin, gaunt lad in a wheelchair. He had a skinhead haircut. He was smiling and obviously happy, but the combination of haircut and bared teeth only served to emphasise his thinness.

"Muscular Dystrophy." Sue sensed Chris's alarm and concern.

"What happened to him?"

"He died about two weeks after that photograph."

There was a silence.

"Isn't that what Karl has got?"

"Yes."

Chris did not want to ask the next question.

"And yes, he will die, soon."

Sarah answered it for him.

"I'm sorry."

She smiled.

"Don't worry. It's a fact of life, and death. It's a lesson to us all. Enjoy life while you can and I am going to enjoy this party."

With that she stood up and went outside and started dancing with the students.

"I didn't realise."

"Why should you?" said Sue.

"Conversations like this are normal round here. We forget sometimes that people outside aren't used to it."

After a couple of minutes Chris finished his drink and they all entered the main room.

He presented prizes and certificates. It seemed that everyone had won something and it took half an hour to get through it all. Chris did a professional job, smiling, encouraging, shaking hands but inside he was in a state of shock. Until now Karl had been just another fan. Okay, he was a special fan. The players always tried harder for disabled kids, but that's what he was just another kid, until now. The kid was going to die. Despite the shock of realising this he smiled and handed out presents.

The presentations complete, people started dancing once more and despite his protestations, Chris was dragged on to the dance floor by Sue and Julie. Chris had begun to relax and enjoy himself so much that when the staff took the students for their lunch he went with them. Normally he would have said his goodbyes by now, but something was keeping him there as if he felt, somehow, that he could make it better. It was a ridiculous notion. He was not going to make anything better but he still felt the need to stay.

He watched the aides helping their charges. At one point, he noticed a girl in a manual wheelchair being pushed out of the room by an aide. Not all of them had electric wheelchairs and he wondered why. There were four carers surrounded by about 20 people who all depended on them for something. Two boys were being fed by one member of staff while another attended to various toileting needs. He realised the responsibility that lay on these three women and one man's shoulders.

He wondered what their wages would be and thought that whatever they earned it wouldn't match the effort or the responsibility of their work. Despite all this, what impressed him most was the humour and liveliness of the scene in front of him. No one here appeared to feel sorry for themselves, or at least if they did, they didn't show it. Then he thought 'of course they wouldn't, you fool, this is a Christmas party'.

Was it a show, a cover up or were they genuinely happy? Apart from the occasional injury he had never had to worry about his health. How did you deal with a permanent disability? How did their parents manage?

"Penny for them."

It was Sarah. He hadn't noticed her approach him.

He smiled.

She smiled back. She could see he was troubled and didn't want him to think that their previous conversation had upset her. The imminent death of her son was something she was dealing with every day of her life. Why would he know?

"Karl would like to talk with you if that's okay?"

Immediately he snapped out of his thoughts.

"Hiya Karl."

Karl beamed as he manoeuvred his chair alongside.

"Thanks."

"What for?"

"My chair. I got it last week."

As they spoke, Sarah slipped away, back to the student support room.

"Why are you thanking me?"

"Because we raised loads of money on that night you came to see me and that helped a lot."

"Oh I see. Well anything I can do to help."

Chris was genuinely pleased that he had been able to help, but at the same time the feeling of gratitude worried him. Why should the kid need to feel gratitude? He needed the damn thing and Chris was annoyed that he could only get it through a charity event. He was angry while this kid was grateful and then something struck him, right between the eyes. He cared.

They started talking about the last season. Chris said "You know I followed your advice. I know my passing has improved. I can feel it in myself."

"I know. I watch you."

Suddenly the young man leant forward towards him in a conspiratorial manner. Chris instinctively did the same.

"I'm going to die," Karl whispered. "You know that, don't you?"

"No," lied Chris, in a whisper. He was unsure what to say. How much did Karl know about his condition? "I didn't..."

There was a pause. What do you say at a moment like this?

"Yes I am." There was another silence.

"Is this a joke?"

Karl's face indicated that he was absolutely serious.

"When?"

"Soon". Any time really. When you get to my age."

He sounded like an old man.

This was not a nice conversation. They were supposed to be enjoying a Christmas party. Chris felt that this was bottled up inside Karl and suddenly he had a minute to tell someone. Was he letting his fears, previously unspoken, emerge for the first time? This was important. He sat there listening to everything his young friend said.

Karl wasn't even upset. He was merely passing on information about his death, his own death. The boy's eyes looked into him.

"I'm worried about my mum. I mean. How will she cope? Since dad died, she's been so busy. She looks after me day and night and there's James and Mel as well. She doesn't stop. What will she do? Will she manage?"

Chris had nothing to say and yet he knew he had to say something, something useful. This was no time for platitudes. Karl was still looking at him as he stumbled over his words.

"Karl. I didn't know. Why? How?"

"My muscles are getting weaker. Every day I get weaker. I don't know how it works, don't want to either. I just am."

"I see." There was another very long pause.

"I need to make certain my mum..."

"I'm sure she will deal with it." Chris blurted out. "She's tough. I can see that."

Chris realised that he must say something that would pave the way for Karl. Karl needed to know that things would be okay.

And then it dawned on Chris that this was not just about Karl's concerns for his mother. He was preparing himself. He was tidying up loose ends. His mind raced down this alley and that. Finally, hesitatingly "Listen, I don't know what to say to make things easier. The next few months are going to be very, very difficult."

"I know."

"For both of you."

"I know."

"And there's no easy way out."

"I know."

Every time Karl said, "I know" Chris felt that he hadn't added anything new to make the boy's situation more comfortable. He needed to get rid of the "I knows".

"Your mum is going to suffer. That can't be avoided."

There was silence. Karl just looked at Chris.

"But all the pain she is going to feel will be softened by the fact that she will know that you loved her."

"I do," he nodded. "I love my mum."

"And she loves you. What we've got to do is make the time you have left fun. You both have to enjoy it."

Chris wanted to avoid platitudes, but had just come up with one.

"Let's make sure that the time you have left is fun." was nice, coming from someone who hadn't got to deal with this situation. But what else was he to say?

"Never mind then?"

They sat there staring into each other's eyes. For the first time Chris saw a crack in the façade that Karl presented to everyone. He was more frightened than he admitted.

"Will you win the World Cup next year?"

"I haven't been picked yet."

"You will be. You were picked in the squad this year weren't you? Next year you'll be in. Your average errors per game are better than any of your rivals and you've scored more tries. Your passing has improved, although you still need to work on your left-sided tackling."

Suddenly the conversation had shifted completely. He wondered whether he had said the right things.

"How do you mean?"

"You always try to tackle with your right shoulder, even when they run at your left. That means your body is in the wrong position and your tackle can be broken. Work on that and you will definitely be selected and you can win. Promise me that you'll win the World Cup."

"I'll do my best."

The young man became agitated. "No. That's not good enough. You have to say you will win it. If you say you'll do your best then doubts can creep in when things get difficult. No one can tell me about positive thinking. Every morning I have to say, 'I will enjoy myself today'. If I didn't I wouldn't even get out of bed."

He stopped in mid-sentence, lost in his thoughts. Chris waited, but Karl seemed mesmerised by himself. Then he lifted his head and stared him fully in the eye.

"I want you to win it. I want you to say you will win it."

"Okay. We'll win it."

"Thanks."

He stopped and thought for a moment. Again Chris waited.

"I wish I was brave and tough like you."

Chris coughed and spluttered.

"Mate, I just play a game and get paid for it. You're far braver than me or any rugby player."

"Am I?"

"I couldn't do what you have to do. You're braver than all of them."

Karl stared at him once more. As the two of them sat there the small CD player began to blast out Tina Turner's *Simply the Best*. It was a song that was often used to introduce teams at the start of a game. As it played Karl began to sing and changed "Better than all the rest," to "Braver than all the rest."

They smiled at each other. The music finished.

"See you later." Karl turned and wheeled himself away.

Chris sat there and watched him go. He watched the frail hand push the control lever and the wheelchair whirred away down the corridor. Chris's gaze followed Karl as he passed through the automatic doors and disappeared from view.

So much had been said about so many important things in such a short time. Karl had just blurted it all out and then left. His fears, his hopes, his wishes all delivered in about three minutes.

"Cup of tea?"

"What?"

"Would you like a cup of tea?"

Julie, the teachers' aide, stood there.

"I'll treat you."

"Yes please."

"Sugar?"

"Er, no thanks."

"Milk?"

"Please."

Julie returned a couple of minutes later, having obtained two cups of tea from the vending machine and handed one to Chris.

They sat there in silence, the busy hubbub of the college continued as students moved around in seemingly non-stop fashion.

"How do you cope?"

"Oh it's always this busy. You get used to it."

"No, I mean Karl. How do you cope? How does he?"

She looked at him and sipped at her tea.

"You just have to. There's no choice."

"But he's only 16."

"Has he told you he's going to die?"

"Yes. Why, isn't it true?"

"Oh yes, it's true enough. It's just interesting that he told you."

"Why?"

"He's never spoken about it to any of us. I think he's getting ready if he's talking about it."

"That's what I thought. I mean I don't know anything about it. It was just a feeling I got. Why would he tell me?"

"Why not, you're his hero? You make things okay for him, for a short while at least. I think he imagines being you and that means being strong and healthy. He told you. You are honoured."

"He's worried about his mum."

"That's useful to know. Thank you. He's not told us that, although they usually are. I suppose it's very difficult to talk. I supposed if it were me I'd try to forget."

"Me too."

"But I suppose that's not possible."

"No."

"How can you forget?"

"Will she cope?"

"Who, Sarah? Probably, they usually do. This situation makes them tough but it's not without its problems."

"Like what?"

"Well, imagine. You have given your whole life for years, absolutely everything. And then the very thing that has drained you totally, stops. Your child's death liberates you. That must be an awful feeling of guilt. No one should have to cope with that. She's had so much to deal with, with her husband dying as well."

"Really? I didn't realise."

"Yes it was a few years ago. He was killed in a car crash."

"Bloody hell."

"Mmm. Life's a bitch."

"For some. How does she cope?"

"I don't know that she does. I've known her for years, before Karl was diagnosed. We used to live in the same street. I don't think she's ever got over Dave's death. I think she's wrapped up in looking after Karl's needs in order to survive and that could be a problem. How will she deal with it when he's no longer here, when she's got to face the reality of losing her son and her husband? One thing's for sure. We're going to find out pretty soon."

He glanced across the room as Sarah and Karl came in. He looked at her and they smiled at one another and he saw the tiredness that he had seen the first time he had met her at the fundraising social.

"I'm taking Karl to his bus."

"Ok love," Julie said as she stood up. They hugged.

"Have a nice Christmas."

"You too."

"Bye Karl."

"Bye."

"I'll come out with you. It's time for me to go and I'll see Karl off. He's been giving me some coaching again haven't you Karl?"

Karl smiled.

"He'll play in the World Cup if he listens to me."

They all laughed.

"Well, you'd better do it then" said Sarah.

They walked out together and Chris watched as the transport staff loaded Karl on to the bus.

"Thanks."

"No problem."

She laughed.

"What?"

"You always say 'no problem'".

She said it in a deep voice, her face contorted to gain the effect.

They laughed.

"Do I? I didn't realise."

"I'm sorry I shouldn't laugh. It's rude."

"No, no, it's all right".

She smiled at him as he accompanied her to her car.

Before he realised, Chris found himself asking if he could see her again. "For a drink, maybe?"

Suddenly she looked flustered. "Er... I have to go. I have to get back for Karl. Er... phone me."

With that she hurriedly got into the car, switched on the ignition and drove off with a wave leaving Chris standing, bemused and apologetic in the drive.

He didn't know why he felt like that. He hadn't done anything wrong, but her reaction had surprised him. She had been so friendly and warm and suddenly it had all changed as if she couldn't get away fast enough. Was he that ugly? She'd told him to phone her, but it had sounded like a 'no thank you' to him. He wasn't even sure why he had asked her. He thought she was attractive enough, but could he have done it because he felt sorry for her? He wasn't sure of himself so he turned towards his car. He would take that as a 'no' then.

Sarah was embarrassed. She was also annoyed with herself. She had not handled the situation well at all. She had acted like a silly 14 year old being asked out on her first date. She was a mature woman and it had been a simple question. "Would you like to go out for a drink sometime?" In truth she had not known what to say. She had not looked at a man since Dave's death. She'd not had time or the energy, or the opportunity for that matter.

Chris's simple question had shaken the cocoon she had built around herself. In devoting herself to caring for her children, and Karl in particular, she had not thought about herself. She liked Chris, even found him attractive, but had been surprised, floored by a simple question and didn't know the answer to it. As she left the college grounds she turned left on to the main road that passed by the car park she had just left and saw Chris moving towards his car. Sarah felt a twinge of guilt and hoped that she hadn't made him feel bad when another thought disturbed her. 'What if he didn't ring?'

Unknown to both of them the plump girl with the hair tied back had been watching from her seat in the refectory. She got up from the table and leaving her food behind her ran down the corridor towards the learning support office. Julie was still there, tidying up and had said her goodbyes to her colleagues. She was enjoying a few quiet moments to herself when Michelle burst into the room nearly frightening the life out of her.

"Julie, Julie!"

"What's the matter? Have you missed your bus?"

"Julie, it's the rugby man and Sarah!"

"Yes?"

"They like each other!"

14. Under pressure

Later that same evening Chris sat in his armchair watching a television programme. It was looking at English football and the World Cup. It was examining the reasons why English football teams seemed to lose penalty shootouts in important competitions, on a regular basis.

The reason for failure was given as the pressure of the situation but he thought, 'Surely both teams faced the same pressure yet England seemed to always lose? Therefore it couldn't simply be pressure and it certainly wasn't just luck. You made luck happen. You made life happen.'

English football, Chris thought, was simply sloppy. They didn't prepare themselves properly like other teams did. They didn't value what they were doing. Life was too easy.

Then, as these thoughts went through his head, another one struck him. Taking a penalty kick wasn't pressure at all. Playing a sport that you loved wasn't pressure.

Pressure didn't exist.

Pressure?

From what?

From facing death before you've started to live?

From worrying about how your mum will cope when you're gone?

From needing to talk to her so much, but realising that she already has so much to deal with that you don't want to burden her any further?

From being so desperate to talk that you blurt out all your hopes and fears to a supposed hero who in reality has got nothing to offer you?

Pressure?

He realised how well off he and other sports people were. Playing a game of football, taking part in a penalty shoot-out wasn't pressure. Being stuck on 99, waiting for your first century in a cricket test match, wasn't pressure either. Nor was there pressure in facing a 16 stone Australian forward charging towards you, trying to score a try against you. Absolutely none of this was pressure.

This was luck.

All these things were self-imposed by people who enjoyed themselves.

This was fun.

It wasn't pressure.

Players, including him, didn't even know the meaning of the word. He pointed the remote and switched the television off. It was all a sham. Television and newspaper reporters, desperate to fill up a few column inches or a timeslot on a sports channel wrote nothing much about nothing much.

He had looked forward to watching this programme and now he saw it for what it was. It was crap. He thought of Karl. Why did some people get such a bad deal? It wasn't fair! He was angry. He was so, so bloody, bloody angry.

In a moment Chris's outlook on life had changed completely.

Sarah sat in her armchair holding the television remote control. She was flicking from one station to the next without concentrating on anything. She was reliving the events of the day and had made a big decision. Yes, she would go for a drink with him. Now that she'd finally convinced herself that it was the right thing to do she was as frightened as a schoolgirl. What if he was annoyed and just said 'no'?

What if he laughed? No he wouldn't do that. He was too nice. What if he'd simply gone off the idea? She flicked channels again. She sat there watching some boring programme about the English football team and flicked again. She looked at the telephone, willing herself to pick it up and pressed the remote again. She sighed. She had not felt like this in years. She was not sure she liked it and then she thought of Dave, hesitated and made herself pick up the phone. Maybe her mum was right. Maybe she had to make herself enjoy something. Maybe she had to go out. What if he changed his mind? She pressed the buttons. It rang a few times. She was about to put it down. He wasn't in. She'd tried and it was just bad luck. It wasn't meant to be.

As the phone neared the receiver she heard a sleepy voice. She jumped. She'd have to speak to him now.

"Hello."

"Chris?"

"Yes?"

"I didn't wake you did I?"

"Yes."

"Oh I'm sorry".

"It's no problem. Who is it?" She was disturbed that he didn't recognise her voice.

"Sarah."

"Sarah who?

"Sarah Burgess, Karl's mum. You know this afternoon?" There was a chuckle on the other end of the line.

Sarah sat upright and smiled as she realised that he had been teasing her. Without realising it she relaxed immediately.

"I was wondering if that offer was still on?"

"What offer?"

"You asked if you could see me again, but I had to go."

"Oh, that."

"Please." She became serious. "Look. This isn't easy for me."

"I know. I was joking. I'm sorry."

82

He realised that she was serious and also vulnerable.

"How about eight tomorrow? We could catch a film?

"That sounds like a good idea. I'll have to check to see if my mum can be with Karl."

"No problem, give us a ring when you know."

Five minutes later she rang back to confirm the arrangements and then sat there smiling. She hadn't been out on a date in years. Come to think of it, she hadn't been out in years.

They sat in the Crown Inn in King Street about a mile outside of the town centre, having just watched *Pride and Prejudice* together. It had been her choice, but he'd said he enjoyed it. He seemed to have done anyway. Chris also had not been out on a date in a very long time.

He stood at the bar ordering his pint and her white wine. He looked at her and smiled. She looked nice in a cream top and jeans. He'd decided he liked her. He brought the drinks across and sat down.

"So what does a professional sportsman do out of season?"

"Not a lot really. Go on holiday I suppose."

"Anywhere nice?"

"No. I didn't go anywhere."

Sarah laughed.

"I see my girls a lot."

"How many do you have?"

"Two. Jenny and Sarah." He smiled at the thought of them and she liked that. "Yeah they're lovely. I get to see them at weekends, but it can be awkward when I'm playing, especially if it's an away game. Caroline complains when I'm not always available."

"Because she doesn't get a break?"

"I can't help it. I have to play when I'm told. It's as simple as that."

"The money's good and she doesn't complain about that." There was a silence and then Chris realised he was talking about his former wife while out on a date. He changed direction.

"I keep myself in shape. I can't let that go. If you lose fitness during the off season, training kills you when you start again and you never quite catch up." He was talking about himself.

"How do you cope?"

"I don't know really. It's just a case of having to I suppose. You get on with it."

"Must be difficult on your own?"

"Yes. I suppose it must be."

There was a silence again.

'Bloody hell.' Chris thought to himself. 'I'm talking about her problems while she's on a night out.'

She smiled at him.

"Did you know you were Karl's hero?"

83

Chris smiled. 'Yes, talk about Karl,' he thought to himself.

"It's funny. I've never felt like a hero. I mean I know how kids feel. I used to do the same, but it's strange. Nice but..."

"Can be a responsibility?"

"Yeah. You're always having to think about what you do. But it is nice. Whenever I find it tiresome I just think about what it will be like when it ends and people start to lose interest. That must be worse, so you have to enjoy it while it lasts."

"Are you thinking of retiring?"

"Not yet, but you do have to make plans. It's not long off, maybe one or two seasons. It depends what the club wants. They have to plan as well."

"Karl won't like that."

"He's fantastic, isn't he? He knows so much."

"He reads about the game all the time. When he was 12 do you know what he asked for as a Christmas present?"

"What?"

"A coaching manual."

"What, the league's coaching manual?"

"Oh I don't know. It was a big thing, black."

"Yes, that's it."

"That's a heck of a read for a kid."

"Well he's read it right through at least twice."

Chris smiled. "Actually, I don't know why I'm surprised. He's a walking encyclopaedia. He knows more than I do about the history of the game."

"Yes. Maybe, in another life he could have been a coach."

"Well, he knows enough." Chris smiled.

"Do you think you'll play in the World Cup?"

"Phew, I don't know about that one."

"He wants you to."

Chris smiled again. "I wish it was that simple. I think I'm probably too old now. This coach has made a point of picking a much younger team than before."

"Well, they'll need some experience to guide them."

Chris wasn't sure whether she was genuinely enthusiastic for him or anxious to ensure her son got what he wanted, or both.

"I must admit last season was one of my best in a long time. I've been working on a couple of things Karl pointed out to me and I can tell I've done better."

"See."

"Whether it's enough I don't know."

Then he thought to himself for a moment. "I don't know that I'm bothered anymore."

"Why?"

84

He took a sip of beer, thought for a moment and then took another. "Since I found out from Karl last week that he's not..."

He hesitated.

"Got long to live?"

"Yes."

He was pleased that she'd said the words for him. 'This woman was strong,' he thought to himself.

"Well, I've questioned things really, the importance of it all. People in sport talk about being under pressure and it's not real pressure. Not like what you and Karl are having to deal with."

"Now listen." Sarah became very serious. "Karl didn't choose this; neither did I and neither did you. This is no one's fault. What's important is how people deal with what they've been given in life. Don't you think it's important, no your duty, that we all make the most of ourselves?"

Chris sat there listening and did not say a word.

"And don't think what you do is not important because some kid is ill. He thinks it's important and if he says it's important then it is. What you do is important to all those fans, those kids who look up to you and are entertained by you. Sure it's just a game, but so what? You make people feel better. Don't ever doubt it. If you've got a chance then you should, must go for it. It's our duty to enjoy life."

Chris stared at her and said "You're right. Thanks."

"Good. It's time I went home."

Chris escorted Sarah to her door. He was determined not to have any teenager-like embarrassment, so he thanked her for a lovely evening, gave her a light kiss on the cheek and left. As he got into the car he was pleased that she was still in her doorway, ready to wave. He waved, drove off and Sarah went in and shut the door.

Sarah had also had a pleasant evening. He had a nice smile, she thought and for once she didn't say to herself 'Just like Dave' but when she thought about him she immediately felt guilty. She found herself defending herself to herself. She'd had a nice night that was all, but still she felt like she was betraying her dead husband. Sarah sighed. She didn't know if she would see Chris again. They hadn't made any arrangements, so she would leave it at that.

Sarah hadn't realised yet that, although she wasn't completely at ease with this new situation, she was beginning to leave the past behind her and look to the future.

Chris shut his front door 15 minutes later, kicked his shoes off, took a beer from the fridge and sat down. He sat there in silence and did not turn on the television as he normally did. He had enjoyed himself more than he had imagined, but he had some thinking to do. When Karl had told him that he would die soon, Chris had been mortified. He had concluded that playing a game for a living was a ridiculous thing to worry about. He had at one point in the last week contemplated packing in the game altogether. Now, tonight, he had been given a completely different perspective and what was more important, he had been given a new lease of life. He wanted that international jersey. It was important to him. It was important to all three of them. Chris was immediately filled with renewed desire and energy. He couldn't wait for the season to start. He had a job of work to do.

They both sat there in their separate rooms thinking about the evening they had just spent together. It had been just a simple date, but it would turn out to be a night that would shape the future for both of them.

15. Lost love

They saw each other with increasing regularity over the coming weeks. Everyone seemed to be pleased about it. Her mum and dad kept telling her how much better she looked. Mel and James were pleased that their mum seemed to be happy, even if it meant that they spent more time indoors with Karl. Their brother was becoming less mobile and had less energy. It was something everyone could see, but no one talked about. Karl was ecstatic. His mum was going out with a local hero, his hero.

How cool was that?

His mates were dead jealous. Everyone at college was always asking him about Chris. His best mate, Robert, the one who still came round to see him, was both chuffed for him and jealous at the same time. Karl and Robert had been friends since nursery school. He was the only able-bodied kid whom Karl still had contact with and the family valued his friendship.

Sarah and grandad took them both to as many home games as possible and Chris provided complimentary tickets. Sarah really enjoyed herself. It was like watching her brothers again, although she didn't scream as much as she used to. She enjoyed being with her son and was not just watching the game. She was watching Chris.

His form had also improved as well. It was as if their relationship – or more accurately friendship – had galvanised him. The press had noticed his improved form and there was increasing talk, as the season progressed into June, that he should be included in the preliminary national squad of 40 players for the World Cup that was to be announced in August.

Chris knew he was playing better than he had done for a couple of years. Some said he was playing better than ever. He had been working on some of the things that Karl had pointed out to him, but he couldn't work out whether his improvement was down to this advice or that he had been given a new motivation in life. He wanted to make Karl happy and was enjoying himself and the time he spent with Sarah.

They had become quite close, but one thing troubled him. He was unsure about sex. At first it hadn't seemed appropriate. Both of them didn't want to enter something that would fizzle out as soon as it started and there were real practical difficulties. The set up at Sarah's wasn't exactly conducive to mad passionate lovemaking. They were always likely to be disturbed. If it wasn't by Karl there was always the chance that the others might be around.

One night they arranged to spend the evening at Chris's. He'd prepared a meal. They had had a couple of glasses of a really expensive red wine that he'd bought specially. Things had gone really well and one thing had led to another. She had returned his kisses as passionately as he gave them, but as he began to unbutton her blouse she stopped him and then started to cry.

She put her head in her hands and sighed.

"Did I do something wrong?"

"No. It isn't your fault. I just can't seem to relax. I'm just not ready," she sobbed.

He put his arms around her.

"It's okay. I understand."

"Maybe later eh?"

She nodded. "I do fancy you," she blurted out.

"Hush. It's okay."

And she lay in his arms for an hour hoping that he meant it. Later he had taken her home. They stood outside her front door and held each other for an age.

"I'd better go in." As she opened the door and he prepared to leave she turned to him and said "I do value us Chris. I do want it to work."

"So do I. I'll phone you."

Sarah went in and ran to her mother like some schoolgirl.

"Whatever's the matter?"

"Oh mam, I think I've lost him!"

June sat her daughter down and listened. It took her back years. She'd lost count of the number of times she'd sat down with her children to sort out some anguish they were feeling about some boy or girl. It was normal teenage stuff and kids recover. She had not expected to be dealing with it again. She waited for Sarah to finish crying and sat there holding her hand.

"What's the matter?"

Sarah blew some air out of her mouth. She and her mum had always been able to talk about anything, but it felt awkward talking about your relationship with your boyfriend when you were 39. She was supposed to be able to deal with things by now.

"Are you having difficulty with sex?"

"Mum!"

"Well, let's get to the point! I'm right aren't I?"

Sarah nodded. "I just can't do it."

"Well it's hardly surprising is it? I mean you're not exactly in the easiest of situations are you? It's bound to put a strain on you isn't it?"

"Has Chris said anything?"

Sarah shook her head. "No. I wish he would. At least we could sort it out."

"Why is it for him to sort out?"

Sarah looked at her mum, but said nothing.

"Well let's see what he might be thinking. If he complains he's probably too demanding and inconsiderate. If he doesn't try it on then you'll think he doesn't fancy you. You're too tired and he's uncertain. I'm sure if you talk to him."

"It's not just that."

"What else is it?"

"I keep seeing his face."

"And you feel guilty?"

Sarah's head bowed again as she grimaced in pain. June held her daughter to her breast. "What do you think he would say?"

"I know. He'd say be happy, but I still miss him mum. I still miss him," and with that she collapsed into sobs. June decided that a firm hand was needed.

"Now, listen to me love. Are you listening?"

Sarah nodded.

June paused. She wanted to tell her daughter to get a grip, to start enjoying herself, to look on the bright side, but she didn't want to sound cruel either. The girl had been through enough, but that said, Sarah had to have some fun in life and she needed someone to show her how to.

"Dave's dead. That's horrible, love. I know how you've suffered. I really do, but you have to let go." She spoke softly and tenderly. "It's time to let go. You're dying inside and he wouldn't want that."

"What about Karl? I can't leave him."

"What? What are you saying love? You won't be giving up on Karl just because you are getting close to Chris. Oh love, that's not true. Karl loves Chris. It's not a problem. Really it isn't. You and Karl can only gain from this. You only have to look at his face to see how much good it's done him having Chris round."

She sat, cuddling her daughter for several minutes when there was a tap on the window.

"That'll be your father wondering where I am." She went to the front door and opened it. Her husband stood there.

"Everything all right?"

She did not let him in.

"It will be in a minute. You go back and I'll be across soon."

John knew his wife well enough to recognise that that meant 'get out of the road I'm dealing with something', and promptly left. He knew when he was not needed. He turned at the gate and said "I'll put the kettle on" but June had already returned to her daughter who had collected herself. She smiled at her mum.

"Bet you think I'm being silly?"

"I don't think that at all. I don't know how I would have managed in your situation, I really don't, but you don't want to throw away something nice because you feel guilty about it. Have a word with him. Take the pressure off. Be friends. He'll understand I'm sure."

"I'd better get back; if you need me?"

"I know where you live." She smiled.

"That's better," and with that she left.

Sarah knew her mum was right, but whether she could do it was another matter. She was torn between her own needs and those of three men: Karl, Chris and Dave. Sorting it out would not be that simple.

June walked back up the street to her house. She turned once to wave to her daughter and told her to go in. She knew that she wouldn't. Sarah would stand and watch until she got to the brow and disappeared from view. She knew something else that she hadn't said to Sarah. There would have been no point. Her daughter was lost in the past because her son had no future.

She had to grasp her chance of happiness, but doing so was easier said than done while Karl was still alive. She stopped as this thought hit her. She was shocked by the truth of it and it took her breath away. She shook her head before re-gathering herself. She knew Sarah would still be watching but she could not look back.

Chris was not happy. Having a woman start to cry the moment he touched her was not exactly a boost to the ego. He did understand, he really did, but it didn't make him feel any better. He wasn't certain what was expected of him. If he didn't try it on would she be disappointed with him? If he did try it on would she turn him down? It was not a good situation. He decided to do nothing. He'd play it cool and wait, but if a better offer came along he'd take it. Then he thought to himself, 'I haven't had any offers,' and laughed out loud. Maybe he was as troubled as she was, perhaps not to the same degree.

After all she'd been through a lot, but he'd not exactly had it easy either. He'd been left by his wife and ultimately divorced. He was living in a flat that had no charm about it whatsoever and he missed seeing his kids on a regular basis. He sat on the sofa and looked at the spartan room that was his lounge. Everything was second hand given to him by friends. Nothing had been bought by him. There was no sense of him in the room or the flat. Although he'd been there for nearly two years it still had a temporary feel about it.

He sat there looking at his mum's old, striped, orange curtains that only just covered the drop of the window and thought 'I hate orange' and 'I don't like stripes.' He looked at the portable grey television that sat on an old stool. The rug had seen better days as had the three-piece suite that had been his brother's cast-off. Other thoughts crept into his head while he sat there. What was he really going to do when his playing days were over? He hadn't made any definite plans until that first night with Sarah in the pub. He didn't know what he was going to do. The world seemed to be closing in on him.

Sitting there he saw his life as he had never seen it before. He was lonely. Ten thousand fans would cheer his name during a match. Articles were written about him in local and national newspapers. He was often interviewed on television.

He was lonely. The only time he felt truly happy was at Sarah's or on a rugby pitch. He decided there and then that he would wait for her and would win the World Cup as he had promised Karl he would. He had to play the best rugby of his career for the whole season and avoid injury even though he was now almost at the end of his career. There were several, young, strong men equally desperate to get into the squad. He had to work harder than ever before.

'No pressure,' he said to himself.

Then he decided to do something else. He decided to buy some new curtains.

16. Upping it

Chris intensified his training regime. He was renowned for his physical strength so he didn't feel he had to work as hard on that. Instead he decided to do an extra five mile run in the week to improve his stamina. This was over and above his training with the club. He had to make certain that he didn't overdo it and tire himself so that his performances dipped, but he wanted to show the national selectors that his fitness was high and his age was not a problem.

He didn't do a simple run though. He had sections where he sprinted and others when he jogged. He varied the lengths of his sprints, breaking them up to try and simulate game situations.

On another day he decided to practice some basic skills. He would do these after the others had left having finished normal training. He was doing simple, but important, things like practicing picking up a ball off the floor at speed. Such simple things could result in a try being scored or saved. They made a difference. He felt he was better prepared and more confident than ever before and every time he finished the session he would see Karl in his head and smile. It was paying off. The new season had gone well. In August he had been selected in the national training squad of 40 players and would then be whittled down to a final squad of 24 at the end of the season. His first task had been completed and he was elated that the national coaching staff had noticed his improved performances.

They weren't the only ones who had noticed.

Don Steer was short and stocky. His full head of hair was white without a hint of grey. In his youth he had played rugby as an amateur and had played for Yorkshire three times in the 1960s. He had had trials with Castleton, but had had only a couple of second team games before he recognised that he would not make it in the top flight. The fact was, he wasn't good enough.

It was strange really. He wasn't angry or devastated. He wasn't even slightly disappointed. He was impressed. He marvelled at how good the top players were. The ordinary fans on the terraces knew the players were good, but they didn't actually know how good they were. He felt proud to have been with them and having had the chance. As he walked home that day he resolved to do two things. The first was to make the most of his talents at amateur level and the second was to qualify as a solicitor, both of which he duly did. Lurking somewhere in the back of his mind was a third, as yet unfocused ambition. That was to get on the board of directors of the club he had followed all his life. If he couldn't play for the club, he was going to run it.

That third ambition was realised long after the other two. He qualified as a solicitor in 1970 and set himself up in his own firm in

1978. It had prospered and then in 1990 he applied to join the board, who had been more than impressed with his offer to inject £100,000 over three years.

Castleton had run into considerable financial difficulties and they virtually bit his hand off. Three years later he was elected chairman on the retirement of his predecessor. After the vote was announced, on 24 November 1994 he sat in the large leather chair at the head of the table and smiled to himself. The other members of the board had left, but he stayed on to savour the moment. He reclined in the warmth of the chair, swinging from side-to-side, as he slowly sipped on a delightful brandy that tasted better than it had ever done before. He looked out from the large expanse of glass that looked out on to the pitch. He vowed then to change things. This was a grand old club. The problem was that it was run like one. It was time to make changes, especially if the club was going to prosper in the future with full-time professionalism.

It offered the opportunity for the sport to move to a new level with players able to develop skills and fitness to new heights. On the other hand, however, it meant that clubs had to find the money to pay for it all. While television funds provided a considerable amount of cash, it still meant that smaller clubs would have even greater difficulty in making ends meet. Rival clubs in big cities with large populations to draw on and a wealth of lucrative sponsorship deals could sign expensive players. Castleton was not in this league and it would not be able to rely on luck as it had before.

In 1995 the board had sat down and formed a strategy for survival. They would establish a youth academy and spend their money on developing their own players rather than spending it on expensive ready-made foreign imports. The next few years saw the club making steady progress. They had finished each season in the top half of the league and had won the Challenge Cup. That was a fantastic occasion and Steer was determined to achieve even more success under his chairmanship.

The problem was how? Under his guidance the board had agreed that the club would be equally loyal and ruthless to its players at the same time. This apparent contradiction was clear in the minds of the directors and had several steps.

First, they would identify and recruit the best young players at an early stage. The second stage would be to give them the best coaching available in order for them to reach their full potential. Next, those who were signed by the club would be paid the maximum that the club could afford. There would be no penny pinching in rewarding and thus keeping good players. Combined with this, players who were not retained would be assisted to move to a club were they would meet with success. Finally when the time was right, they would transfer players before their 'sell-by date' had arrived and replace them with a young player. This meant that the team would be refreshed and players would leave while still performing well. They would not be kept to a point where the fans started to complain because they quickly forgot past glories.

Steer was pleased with the results, but time was now moving on. Seven years is a long time to be at the top in rugby league with its heavy demands on the body. The first crop of youngsters reared on full-time professionalism would now be ready to move on.

Chris Anderton was obviously not one of this group. He was a bit older than the others, having been recruited before full-time professionalism had formally started and the modern policy had been developed. It was therefore only right that he should be the first player to be formally reviewed. Steer was a longstanding admirer of Anderton's no nonsense approach. He was a skilful player, but not the best. He was fairly fast, but not the fastest and was as strong as an ox, but not the strongest. Steer rated him as probably fourth or fifth in the country in those categories, but that actually made for a high level of consistency. There were stronger players, but not as fast. There were faster players, but not as skilful. What these attributes combined to do was to make Anderton into a thoroughly good club player without reaching international class. Added to these attributes he had tremendous stamina and seemed to be able to keep going, but nothing lasts forever.

Anderton was now 31. Over the last two seasons he had suffered three injuries keeping him out for a total of 15 out of 60 games. It was also felt by some, but not all, that his enthusiasm was waning. Anderton's fans would have said that this wasn't true. The player hadn't been given enough time to recover from injury. If a player comes back too soon, they inevitably suffer another injury. The chairman was not so sure. Anderton was beginning to creak. It was time for him to go.

He leaned across to the intercom. "Margaret?"

"Yes, Mr Steer?"

Could you make an appointment with Chris Anderton? I need to speak with him."

"Yes, Mr Steer."

"Oh, and Margaret?"

"Yes, Mr Steer?"

"Invite his agent as well."

"Er, yes Mr Steer."

'That was strange,' thought Margaret. 'They only involve agents when contract negotiations are made and Chris's was not due. The only other time agents were involved was during transfers and they wouldn't be transferring Chris Anderton, now would they?'

Chris had an inkling of what the meeting would be about. His agent had called him to say that Don Steer had invited them both for a meeting about the future. Chris smiled at the word 'invite'. Steer was a nice enough fellow, but he was ruthless when he had to be. 'Invite' was not really the word he would have used, but in the absence of anything else he understood.

Sarah nearly exploded when she heard the news.

"But they wouldn't sell you, not now. You're playing so well and you've just got into the Great Britain squad."

"That's probably the best time, before I go off. We only last so long you know."

"Yes, but you've given your whole career to the club. They should look after you."

"I don't think that comes into Mr Steer's calculations."

"What are you going to do?"

"Wait and see what he says. I can't do anything else."

"Karl will be upset. I can't believe that you're so calm about it."

Chris wasn't calm. He was seething. He was furious at Steer's attitude, although he hadn't done anything yet. He just didn't need a distraction, not now.

James Brady, his agent, had told him to expect the worst because Castleton were about to initiate changes to the squad. He had spoken with Brady at length. Chris still genuinely believed he had two good years left in him. It was true that he had suffered a couple of injuries in the last two seasons, but he was now over them. He'd played most of the games last year. He felt good, better than he had done for a number of months.

He wasn't yet over the hill. He wasn't. All day he had been thinking that he wasn't out of it. Surely he was still good? Sarah was right. He was in the international squad. They wouldn't get rid of him would they? Then his own words came back to him. "Maybe it was the best time to transfer him." Then he would have moments of doubt. Perhaps they were right. Perhaps he was past it. Maybe he had been deluding himself when he believed that Karl was his new motivation.

What was the worst thing an ageing sportsman could do? It was to delude himself. Every player knows that the end has to come sooner or later, but the problem is spotting it and then accepting it

They fail to spot that their time is up for a number of reasons. It could be that they still enjoy what they do but can't do it quite as well as before. It could be that they feel alright, but the new generation come along and simply blow them away before the older performers have a chance to realise it. Sometimes the problem is financial. People carry on longer than they should because they need the money that they have become used to or and worst of all they don't finish because they are frightened of the alternatives.

What will they do? Where will they go? How will they cope with being an 'ex'? Whatever reason there is nothing sadder than a world champion boxer being battered by some kid who has achieved nothing in comparison. There is nothing worse than a world-class goalkeeper letting in one soft goal too many or a sprint champion not qualifying for a final.

In rugby league there is nothing worse than having someone zip past your defence as if you weren't there and hearing the crowd collectively doubt your right to be in the team. The skill is to know when to bow out at the top with the crowd cheering your every move and your colleagues patting you on the back. The skill is in being able to say to the directors, 'Thanks but no thanks' as they offer you another year.

And so it was in a cloud of confused thoughts that he went to the meeting. His car crackled over the stones in the car park. As he got out, he saw something he hadn't noticed before. The players' cars were different to his. He saw that the cars were a mixture of sports cars or fast saloons. His was a family car, a practical car useful for picking up his kids and all their stuff for weekend visits. The other family cars belonged to the coaches. The ageing process, accelerated in professional sport where you were past your best at 33, was clearly identified in the car park.

He was surprised that he hadn't noticed it before, but now given his situation, he realised that he needed to think differently. Maybe the management were right. Maybe it was time.

As he stood outside the boardroom, he looked at the photographs of past players that decorated the walls. The club's first captain, Ernest Williams, stood proudly in 1889. The whole wall was filled with old pictures of players from the past. Was he to become one of them? Did they see their end come any better than he had? He shared more in common with the fading face in the picture than with the future. Suddenly he felt very old and outdated. Rugby league was not his future. He needed a new path but what? Where to?

The door to the boardroom opened. Paul O'Sullivan, the vice-chairman, stepped out and shook their hands.

"Gentlemen," He beamed. "Come in."

They entered the room.

In all his time at the club, Chris had never been in the main boardroom. When he signed his contracts it had always been in the chairman's office. He'd never been invited into this place. 'This isn't my club,' he thought. 'I'm an employee.' He'd never thought of it like that before and felt miserable. He was a piece of meat about to be released once its sell-by date had gone.

The room was light and airy and modern. The walls were pale, with a row of tall, narrow windows looked out onto the training pitch which was a hive of activity as players darted about on training routines in the sunshine. He was ushered onto a seat which matched 11 others apart from the one at the head of the table. Although in the same simple style, it had a higher back as befitted the seat of a chairman.

In this chair sat Don Steer, beaming across at James. He didn't know whether this was a good sign or not for Mr Steer always smiled whether the news was good or bad. O'Sullivan sat on Steer's right. The chairman stood up and shook both their hands vigorously.

"Would you like a drink? Tea, coffee or perhaps a sherry?"

Both men declined.

"Very well, as you wish." The formalities over Steer's face became serious. His opening words were, "Chris. You know that I am a great admirer of yours."

Chris sensed a "but" coming.

"But the fact is that at sometime in every player's career there comes a time when it is necessary to review his situation. I, we, I mean the board, feel that the time has now come to review your future."

He was out. He knew it. No matter how sweetly Steer dressed it up, he knew he was out. Suddenly, in the blink of an eye, 15 years were finished. One day you're in, the next moment you're out. He felt sick but was determined not to show it. He saw his career becoming faded as those old photographs outside.

"We need to review our situation and I'll be straight with you. We've had an enquiry from Wigan. They have asked permission to approach you."

Chris had not anticipated that. He'd expected to be told that he was finished. Playing for Wigan, one of the most famous clubs in the whole rugby world, was not to be sneezed at.

"Wigan?"

"Aye."

Chris and Brady exchanged glances but said nothing. They sat there taking it in.

"Why?"

Steer laughed. "Well, you've been playing well lad. Some would say sensationally. Maybe at 31 they want an experienced player who can take them forward."

"What did you say to them?"

"I said we didn't want to lose you, but we wouldn't stand in your way." There was a pause. "It's up to you Chris."

"Is that it?"

"Aye, it's really that simple. You take some time to think about it. There's no harm in listening to their offer."

Steer leant forward with his elbows resting on the table, his hands clasped together. His eyes wandered from one man to the other. "As I said there's no need to rush." He turned to Brady, "Shall I give them your number?"

"They should have it, but by all means do so when you give them permission to contact us."

"Good."

"Well, that's all there is gentlemen." Steer moved round to the door and shook hands once more. He held Brady's hand tightly "It goes without saying that we don't want the press to get hold of this do we?" Brady smiled and nodded.

"Of course not."

Then he shook Chris's hand, "We don't want to lose you, we really don't, but it could be a wonderful opportunity for you. Let me know in, say, a week?"

Chris nodded silently and left. Chris and Brady walked past the memories hanging on the wall, down the steps and out of the main entrance. As they walked to their cars his agent turned to Chris.

"What do you want to do?"

"Nothing as yet," replied Chris.

"Nothing?"

"That's right. Nothing."

"Are you not interested in a move to Wigan? Could be big money you know?"

"Of course I know."

"I just need to think. Don't do anything and don't say anything to the press."

"Of course not."

Chris and his agent said their goodbyes. Chris drove home. He had a lot of thinking to do.

Steer shut the door behind them went to the drinks cabinet and poured two Sherries. He passed one to his colleague and they touched glasses. He moved over to the window where he could see the academy players going through their paces.

He was pleased with himself. He knew how to get what he wanted from people. It was true that he didn't want to lose Chris. He was a nice lad, but the fact was that he'd had an offer of £80,000 for an ageing player whom he was going to replace anyway and the lad had just been drafted into the international squad. He probably wouldn't make it into the team, so now was the best time to sell.

He chuckled to himself. The fact that he'd approached Wigan in the first place and offered Chris's services just served to confirm what a shrewd operator he was. He was really pleased that Chris had been doing those extra training sessions. They'd just made the club £80,000.

17. Jumping ship

The first approach came to him through his agent who relayed it to him by telephone. "They're talking a two year contract on £80,000 a year with the likelihood of an assistant coaching position as well on retirement."

This was very flattering. The trouble was it would mean moving to Wigan. He wasn't sure he wanted to do that. In fact he was no longer sure he wanted to coach. The more he thought about it the more he realised that he had become stale. He'd been going through the motions until he met Karl.

Karl was a completely new factor in the equation. Since he'd met Karl his whole view on life had changed and while he had promised to achieve one more thing as a player, he was no longer certain about what the future held. At the same time he was mindful of the fact that he'd had a big offer before and turned it down. He'd lost a lot of money as a result and as he could see the end of his career looming money became an important consideration. A lack of ambition had also cost him his marriage, or at least had been a factor in its end. He didn't want to make a similar mistake. How strong was his relationship with Sarah? What would happen when Karl was no longer here? If he declined Wigan's offer could he be left with no club and no Sarah?

He was confused and worried. If he did sign for Wigan what would Karl think? What would Sarah do? For the first time as a professional sportsman he was thinking not only about himself, but about others. He picked up the telephone.

"Sarah, can I come round? I need to talk to you."

"I see." Sarah just sat there. For a time she stared at the table.

"Well?"

She looked at him. "Well what?"

"What do you think?"

"I don't know; it's up to you. It's a great opportunity. What will you do?"

Sarah was confused by her feelings. On the one hand she had been uncertain about her feelings for Chris. She had found herself growing increasingly fond of him, but their inability, her inability, to take their relationship a stage further had begun to worry her deeply. Of course her feelings were understandable and justifiable. She was under a lot of personal strain that would have destroyed many women, but the problem had begun to sew seeds of doubt in her as to whether the relationship would ever be strong enough.

On the other hand she now found herself worried that she might lose him, that the attraction of pastures new would break the frayed ties between them. She didn't want to lose him, but she wasn't sure she wanted to, could, keep him. Now she feared that events might conspire to force her to make decisions she wasn't ready to make. She stared at the table.

Chris was also confused. He had a great opportunity in front of him. It was one that would map out his future and make his life certain and secure, prosperous even, but he wasn't sure he wanted it. He needed Sarah to say, "Please stay."

He waited.

She said nothing.

The silence was broken by the arrival of the school bus. Sarah got up to bring her son in. Chris stood on the front step watching the daily routine unfold. He was touched by the dedication and professionalism of the staff and Sarah's strength and fortitude. 'She deals with things so well,' he thought, but every day she must have been traumatised by the difficulties she, they, all faced or was he wrong? Was this simply life and they got on with it?

He admired Sarah tremendously, but their relationship was stuck and he wasn't certain what to do about it. He had vowed to stay and help. Now this opportunity had come along. Should he take it? If he decided to stay and then Sarah decided that they had no future, would he lose everything? Could there be no job and no Sarah? Events were forcing him to make decisions he didn't feel ready to make.

All these thoughts raced through his head in the time that it took Karl to get off the bus and drive down the path. He came towards Chris, but did not smile.

"Wigan?"

"What?"

"Bloody Wigan!"

Karl bounced over the threshold into the lounge. Sarah followed him in, casting a quizzical look in Chris's direction.

Karl was obviously upset. He was dressed in a shirt and shorts, but was still perspiring with anxiety and frustration. "Wigan!" he said as if he were chewing razors.

"How do you know?"

"So it's true?"

Chris could see himself gawping at Karl.

"Nothing has been decided by anyone. How did you know?"

"It's all round college. Everyone's talking about it. It's in the paper!"

Right on cue the *Castleton Mail* popped through the letter box. Sarah retrieved it from the hall and turned to the back page.

"Anderton set for Wigan move?" covered the top of the back page in large type. The article said that he had been unavailable for comment. It presented Steer as being sad at the possible loss of a valued player. It went on to say that despite this the club would not stand in his way if he wanted to improve his fortunes elsewhere and that the club would continue to build for the future. It looked like Chris was angling for a way out of the club and was now avoiding the press.

Chris took hold of the paper and continued to gawp. Only two, three people knew about this besides himself, Steer, O'Sullivan, and Brady. However, there was also the entire Wigan board and possibly the rest of the Castleton board.

In fact, there were quite a lot of people who could possibly leaked the information, but why? Nothing was agreed. Steer had specifically asked that no mention be made to the press. Maybe he was worried about the fans' anger if it got out that the club was trying to offload him. Did he want to make it look like Chris wanted the move? Was Steer trying to present it as a fait accompli and shifting the 'blame' onto Chris? Was Brady trying to increase the price and improve the deal? Who, why?

Chris was annoyed. He felt that he had been a loyal club servant but it didn't look like that. Chris looked at Sarah and her son. "I only found out about this yesterday. You know that Sarah. That's why I came to see you, but nothing's been agreed. Honestly. I wasn't coming here to say goodbye or anything like that. This is press crap."

"Okay," said Karl. "But are you going to go?"

"I don't know. That's why I came here to talk to your mother about it. I do have to start thinking about my future. I'm not going to be around much longer."

"Neither am I."

Chris had nothing to say to that. The simple transfer of a player, whether real or not, was an everyday matter in any sport, but it had suddenly assumed major proportions to a boy whose health was deteriorating rapidly and who would probably not survive the year.

To Karl it looked like his hero, his student even, the person who had unwittingly kept him alive these past few months was about to jump ship.

18. Heading north

The local newspaper was not the only media outlet taking note of the situation at Castleton. Lewis Jenkins was an experienced sports features writer. As a younger man he had played first class rugby union for Swansea. He had also played once for Wales until a serious knee injury finished his promising career.

He was a columnist on the national *Sunday Reporter*, his work having developed from his original rugby union reporting. Then one day the sports editor called him into his office

"Here's a story just waiting to be told. There's this disabled kid who appears to be the person behind the rejuvenation of a player, Chris Anderton, the rugby league international. It could be a big human interest story. It's not just about sport. So you need to check it out. This kid's dying, so there'll be a lot of human drama, tragedy etc. You get it? So I want you to check it out, okay?"

He sat down at the computer and began to read articles from the local press. The turnaround in this Chris Anderton's career did seem remarkable. There was even an article and a photograph of the kid involved. So he was the motivation behind Anderton's improved performances? He studied the picture. The young man was smiling at his hero. It was a nice picture, but he looked gaunt.

Then he typed "Muscular Dystrophy" into a search engine on his computer. Several websites came up and he ploughed through them and started to understand the condition. He paused and reflected on what he'd read. "Poor bugger. Not even the English deserve that."

Maybe this was going to be a better story than he had first thought. His first task was to interview Chris Anderton. Reading the background material he learned about the player's change in fortunes. He logged onto the Castleton RLFC website and downloaded a player profile of his interviewee. He then picked up the phone to speak to the club press officer and arranged an interview.

He travelled by train from his Swansea home. He always travelled by train on such journeys. He would do the interview and type it up on the return journey. First class travel was therefore required. It wasn't a bad life really, for a working class boy 'done good'.

He was to interview Chris Anderton the next day, but before that he wanted to get a feel of the community where he lived. So he'd booked into a comfortable hotel just outside the town centre.

He was going to watch the Castleton versus Huddersfield match that evening prior to meeting Anderton. He had made a note to visit the Rugby pub before the game as it seemed obvious that it would be a major centre for the club's fans.

At the hotel he showered and had a meal before strolling down to the Rugby pub. It was a pleasant summer evening and he enjoyed the walk.

As he headed towards the ground he saw people wearing red and white heading in the same direction. He could hear the pre-match announcements blasting out of the tannoy system and through the gap between stands he could see terracing, sparsely occupied by early arrivals, probably watching a schoolboy match before the main game.

He checked his watch. It was just before seven. He had enough time for a pint before the game started, enough time to sample the atmosphere. Crossing the front car park of the pub, he entered a large, open plan, main lounge. He was greeted by a wall of red and white shirts, interspersed by the Huddersfield colours. The match was a local derby. Huddersfield was the nearest club to Castleton. However, the club shirts seemed to mix, some supporters of both teams clearly knew each other. What struck him once more was the similarity with his own background. This was not like football. Of course there was an 'edge', but there was no threat of violence.

He decided, on the spot, to try and interview someone. He had enough time. Anyway it wouldn't matter too much if he missed the start. He approached a couple sat in the corner. He picked them out because she wore Huddersfield's colours and he wore the red and white of Castleton.

Jenkins introduced himself, and asked "So how come you're in Castleton colours and you're in Huddersfield's?"

The woman replied, "I come from Huddersfield and my husband, he's an arsehole." She laughed out loud.

"And it doesn't cause any problems?"

"It will tonight if we lose", the woman joked. The conversation carried on for a few more minutes and after Jenkins had decided it would go no further, politely thanked them and stood up to go.

As he stood up the man paused. He turned to Jenkins, "Are you doing a story about Karl?"

"I am interviewing someone, yes."

"The disabled lad?"

"Er, yes."

"I know them. They're lovely people." He stood and thought again.

"Be nice. They've had too much going on for one of you journalists to make things worse. It's not fair." The man looked him in the eye. "Be nice."

Jenkins smiled and said that he would do his best. Then he was alone. While he sat there thinking about the two comedians the pub emptied. The pub was quiet within half a minute.

"You not going to the match then?" asked the barmaid as she began clearing away hundreds of bottles and glasses.

"In a minute" he said. He thought of the boy he was yet to meet. People obviously knew about him and cared. Maybe there was the possibility of a decent story after all. Lewis Jenkins, the professional reporter, made a note.

He left the pub and turned leftwards towards the ground. Passing over a small bridge he turned rightwards through the main gates. Walking past the training ground he headed towards the red turnstiles. It was obvious that the ground was ageing and had not seen any real development since the 1960s. Once more he was struck by the similarity between his own town and this one. There had simply not been the funds made available to either code of rugby that had been received by football.

The cinders crunched beneath his feet. A man and a boy ran past him as the crowd could be heard welcoming the players onto the pitch. The father was sorting money out as he shuffled the boy into a turnstile simply marked "£10."

He entered through the same turnstile as the father, paid the £18 admission fee and came out the other side towards the pitch. He had not used his press pass because it would have meant sitting in the press box. He wanted to feel the real atmosphere. He'd claim the money back on expenses.

Passing a hot dog stand on the left he entered the terracing and stood at one of the corners of the ground. Ignoring the game for a minute he watched the people. To his left a covered terrace housed a considerable crowd. To his right, stretching behind the posts the terracing was uncovered. Across the other side of the pitch was a brick fronted stand containing the only area of seating. This was the main focal point of the ground. The words "Castleton RLFC" ran along the centre of the wall in large white letters on a red background.

As he watched, an almighty roar swept over him as a player in a white shirt with a red band sped towards the try line and dived into the corner. Castleton had scored.

For the rest of the evening he spent his time trying to watch and listen to the people. His instincts, however, made this increasingly difficult as he kept being distracted by the game. Of course, he knew the game. He had watched it many times on television and could not resist the tension and drama of any sporting event. Throughout the lead switched between the two teams. He was struck by the intensity and ferocity of the game. Around the hour mark Castleton established a solid lead.

He decided to move around the ground. He stepped onto the walkway. On reaching the far end he climbed the steps moving under the roofed terracing behind the far goal. Although supporters of both clubs mingled together in a way that had become unheard of in most football grounds, the majority of the Huddersfield supporters had gathered here. He stood watching them. They were ordinary working class people who were extremely knowledgeable about their sport. He made a note.

As the hooter signalled the end of the game, the defeated Huddersfield fans saluted their team's brave efforts. As they trundled off to begin their journey home, Jenkins stayed behind to watch the stadium empty. Litter drifted past him driven by a gentle breeze. Groundsmen were already out sweeping the terraces and checking the pitch for damaged turf. Across the far side he could see the lights of the restaurant and hospitality boxes still housing corporate guests. This was a big operation.

Finally, he decided he'd seen enough. He left the ground, decided against a return to the pub and returned to his hotel. He had to prepare for the interview the next day. He was always meticulously prepared, but this time he had to collect his thoughts. He had some questions to ask that he had not even thought of prior to his visit. Before he knew it he was back in his room. He had been impressed by the game and the people. This game was well supported by knowledgeable people. It mattered to the communities where it was played. Rugby league was a highly athletic spectacle played by extremely fit and skilled players.

He opened his briefcase and pulled out the profile of Chris Anderton. He read it through once more before moving on to the article about Karl and his mother. This said that Karl was a mad keen rugby fan who attended every home game. It described his detailed knowledge of the game he'd never played. There were a couple of references to Chris Anderton, who said how clever he thought Karl was, but only a hint of Karl affecting Anderton's playing. That was what he had to pursue the next day. He had to get the human aspect into the article. He had to show how a disabled kid was helping a star improve. Jenkins sat down to his computer and started to type.

19. A story

Jenkins rose the next morning at eight. He had ordered three morning newspapers, one broadsheet and two tabloids. He scanned the sports pages for references to last night's game. Only the broadsheet had any sizeable reference to it and even here it was still dwarfed by articles on soccer and rugby union. Of the two tabloids, one only gave the result and the other ignored it completely. He was surprised that a major sporting event watched by nearly 17,000 people was hardly covered, but then Fleet Street was a long way away.

His appointment was for 10.30am. Perhaps it was too early after last night's game, but as the taxi entered through the same main gate he had entered through the previous night he recognised Chris Anderton immediately. Stood by the shop entrance dressed in a Castleton tracksuit, he stood there talking to a young woman who looked as if she worked in the shop. As he got out of the taxi, Anderton nodded towards the girl who returned to the shop.

Smiling, Anderton limped towards him, hand outstretched.

"Mr Jenkins?"

"Lewis, please."

They shook hands.

"Took a knock last night?"

"Yeah. Bit of a dead leg I think. It'll soon wear off."

"I enjoyed the game."

Anderton opened the main doors and ushered Jenkins through.

"Did you come? You should have said."

"I didn't want to be a nuisance. I enjoyed watching from the terraces."

They entered an office and sat down. "Fancy a cup of tea?

"Yes please."

Anderton nipped out of the office and returned two seconds later.

"Janice will bring one in."

"Do you mind if I use a tape recorder?"

"No. Fine."

Jenkins checked the volume level and was about to ask his first question when Janice entered carrying a tray. She smiled politely and left. Chris grinned and swivelled round in the office chair. The sweep of his legs seemed to fill the entire width of the room and Jenkins couldn't help noticing that his shoes must have been at least size 13.

The atmosphere was relaxed and Anderton was easy to talk to. Already he could feel himself warming to this character. After pouring the tea and taking a biscuit, Jenkins switched on his tape recorder.

"Okay?"

"Okay."

"What about the young lad?"

106

"What lad?"

"Karl."

Chris smiled. "Bloody hell, how do you know about him?"

"I'm a reporter. I do research and I've got sources."

Chris laughed, and then he stopped and became serious for a moment. "He's just a lad."

"He's more than just a lad isn't he?"

"He's a lad who's going to die."

"Why?"

So Chris explained the situation. He talked about meeting him and how much he admired him. He told Jenkins about how he'd met Karl, and about raising money for a new electric wheelchair. He talked about Sarah, her courage and perseverance and how strong and vulnerable she was at the same time. Jenkins didn't need to ask a question. Answers were pouring out.

"Can I ask a question?"

"Yes?"

"Is he the reason your form has turned round like it has?"

"How do you mean?"

This was the first time in the interview that he had asked a direct question, but it was fundamental. "Well often when a player, in any sport, gets to the age of 30-something, he is transferred before his sell-by date expires and the club ends up carrying someone who is living on former glories. These players then go on to their new clubs, albeit sadly, to play some of the best games of their lives. They seem to flourish in the new found responsibilities that fall upon an older player. That hasn't happened to you. You're still here, but things, everything about you seems to have improved."

Anderton sat there, thoughtful. He was taken aback by the question. He was surprised and couldn't think of an answer so thought in the hope that an answer would come to him, but none did.

Jenkins sat there waiting. "I ask the question because it raises a very important issue. Who is helping whom? Are you helping the boy or is he helping you?"

"I didn't get involved to help myself." Chris said quietly.

"I didn't think for one minute that you did. I'm not saying that your intentions have been anything but honourable, but things happen don't they? You set out on one path and it takes you somewhere, but you don't know where that will be or what it will mean. It's not a bad thing. It's a good thing. Maybe it's your reward for doing a totally good deed. Maybe you've been given something because you deserve it?"

Chris had become quite upset, not because he had thought that he was helping this boy to serve his own ends, but because in the course of the interview he understood how important Karl was. He'd been living it, but knowing it wasn't the same. Everything good that had happened to him in the last nine months had been down to him.

The boy had changed his attitude fundamentally and not only about rugby. The boy had changed his life and, while before, he had admired him in a sort of patronising way, he now viewed him differently. This boy was not a victim to be pitied. This boy contributed. He was showing him the real meaning of life. He was showing him about bravery, about perseverance, about never ever giving up. Above all, he recognised that while at first he had taken Karl's advice with a little grain of salt, the truth was that he had been right. His skills had improved. In that same moment he realised that, even at this late stage it was possible to improve further if he took Karl seriously. He hadn't seen it before, but he now knew that the boy was in charge. The boy was helping him in every way.

Jenkins watched quietly as these thoughts raced through Chris's mind. It was obvious from the pained look on his face that he had hit a nerve. "Am I right?"

Chris coughed. "Yes. I hadn't thought too much about it before, but you are right. He's been coaching me." This was the first time that Chris had told anyone that Karl had been directing his extra training.

"A 16 year old kid is coaching an international player?"

Chris nodded seriously.

"How?"

"He watches me and advises me on how I can improve."

"But he can't play."

"Being a good player doesn't make you a good coach. Some good players don't know why they are good. They just are. In fact being in a wheelchair probably helps him."

"How?"

"He watches. He sees. He studies."

"But how can he appreciate the demands and difficulties?"

"Oh he knows about difficulties." Chris smiled. "He could teach any athlete about difficulties. He knows how hard it is to catch a ball, let alone anything else. Believe you me, he knows."

Jenkins didn't know what to say. He could see that Chris had a point, but still. It was obvious that the interview was played out. His mind raced on as he glanced at his watch. There were still five hours before his train was due to leave.

"I'm meeting Karl and his mum at 1pm. I need a photograph and to ask him a few questions. Is it far?"

"No, I'll take you."

Twenty minutes later, they were pulling up outside Sarah's house. Jenkins spoke with Karl for over an hour. "Chris tells me that you've been giving him advice on how to improve?"

"Yes."

"How have you learnt all this?"

"I read books, magazines, watch TV, all sorts really. I also keep records on players to monitor how they are doing."

"Can you show me?"

Karl switched on his computer and showed him a bewildering array of files. He had files on each of Castleton players detailing such things as recurring mistakes along with suggested means of improvement. It was a dossier on individual and team performances that would have put many a professional coach to shame.

"This is very impressive Karl."

"Yes."

Jenkins looked round the room.

The walls were covered in newspaper articles and posters including one of Chris. The boy certainly knew what he was talking about. Jenkins looked at Karl. He had been genuinely impressed with the boy's, no young man's, work.

His enthusiasm was obvious, but the interview had been difficult. Karl's answers were very limited. Often he had given only one word answers. It seemed to Jenkins that all this dedication was in the past and that the present took a lot of effort.

He had only just met this young man. He had been impressed by him, but as he sat there on the edge of his bed an awful thought struck him. Karl hadn't got long.

An hour later they were travelling back to the railway station. Jenkins had taken a photograph of Karl. He had taken one of Chris and Karl together. All-in-all he had two very productive interviews. He was more than pleased.

He and Chris shook hands at the platform gate. He passed by the official checking tickets and then stopped and turned to Chris.

"Will you win the World Cup?"

Chris smiled and nodded. "I have to."

He said goodbye to Chris and boarded the train. He had been surprised and impressed by his whole visit and in particular by a 16 year old boy.

What a story this could be. He could see the headlines already forming, the human interest story that transcended mere sport but would touch the soul of every caring person in the land. Maybe there was even a book in it? He'd got a real story. He could make something out of this. He set about making notes, lots of notes.

20. Famous

Jenkins had explained to everyone concerned that he was not certain when the article would be published. There were still several weeks before the World Cup which was set to commence in the first week of October and last for five weeks. It would be the editor's decision if and when the article would run. It wasn't guaranteed, although he was fairly sure that the angle he would put on it would ensure that it did.

Karl could not be convinced, however, of the possibility of any delay, let alone that the article might not appear. Two weeks passed by. On both Sundays, Karl left their house full of hope and excitement only to return in a foul mood when he had discovered that there was nothing in the paper. The only thing that had pleased Karl in that fortnight was the fact that Chris had made it into the Great Britain final squad of 24 players. He was going to play in the World Cup!

The following Sunday he went out as soon as Sarah had finished feeding and dressing him. She was concerned at the speed at which he shot round the corner towards the newsagents. She had always let him be as independent as possible, but feared for his safety in his weakened state. She tried to rationalise the fact that the excitement was good for him. It was true that it was giving him a sense of purpose, but at the same she didn't want it to make him ill. He was so looking forward to seeing Chris play in the World Cup and she didn't want him to miss it.

She pottered about the house, tidying up, occasionally looking out of the window then she washed the dishes. Again she looked out of the window, but there was no sign of her son. If the truth were known she was almost as excited as he was. She had wanted to go to the shops with him, but had decided to let him go by himself.

Now, after nearly 40 minutes, she was becoming concerned. He should have been gone for no more than 15 minutes, 20 at most. Concern turned to fear and fear turned to panic. What if the excitement had proved too much? What if his heart had given out? What if he'd been mugged? He had five pounds on him and he wouldn't be able to defend himself. Sarah slipped out of her slippers and jumped into her trainers in one smooth movement. She flew out of the door, out of the gate and round the corner. Two hundred yards of lung bursting effort brought her to the shopping centre that served the estate. Only the newsagent was open. There was no sign of Karl. She almost fell into the doorway only to see Karl's face beaming.

Joan, the newsagent, was at Karl's side holding the paper open for Karl. Sarah had just sufficient energy left to appreciate that picture. He looked so happy and proud. There was a photograph and a full-page article headed by the words, "League international inspired by disabled young coach." The photograph showed Karl, Chris and herself. Her immediate thought was not about the rugby at all. 'We look so happy,' she said to herself.

"Wow. We're famous," she said and Karl chuckled, full of glee, until he started to cough. Sarah patted him and eventually he stopped.

"Okay love?"

"Oh yeah," he said "We're in the paper," and he smiled again. They went back to their house slowly. Sarah's legs were wobbly after her exertions and Karl's coughing had slowed him down physically if not mentally. They enjoyed a lovely 15 minutes together, chatting about the article and the World Cup. Karl checked twice that she had booked tickets for the Final. Chris had already told them not to worry about the earlier rounds as he would get them tickets when he was playing. Sarah didn't think that Karl would manage to attend every match because of the travelling, so she and Chris had agreed to play it by ear. She wanted to make certain he was well enough to go to the Final if Great Britain got through. Karl just wanted to go.

Sarah smiled at him as she watched him negotiate the entrance to the house. He deserved his moment of fame and she was very proud of him. When they got in they found Chris waiting in the kitchen with Mel and James. He was beaming as much as Karl was. "Well, what do you think?"

"It's great isn't?"

"Did you know it was going to be today?"

"No, I just saw it half an hour ago. I haven't even read it yet. I just came over here straight away. It's great isn't?"

They looked at it together while Sarah read it out.

Things changed after that. Nothing was said but Chris sensed a change in the atmosphere. Sarah was pre-occupied with Karl's failing health and obviously had less time for him. He understood that. He too had his own concerns. Although they were nothing as fundamental as the problems Sarah faced they were nevertheless important. He had to fulfil a promise he had made to a dying boy.

The combined weight of problems meant that they started to see less of each other. Their relationship just seemed to get too difficult to manage and Chris was uncertain how much she wanted him to be involved. Their relationship would have to wait. In their different ways, they both had to fulfil their obligations to Karl.

He had told the board that he was not ready to decide about the transfer yet. He wanted to focus on the World Cup. If the board didn't like it, then it was tough. Sarah and Karl accepted his explanations about the possible transfer and Karl was even able to laugh at it. He came to understand that, even if the stories of Chris's supposed transfer weren't true, he did need to look after his future. The trouble for Karl, however, was that it confirmed how little say he now had in the events that surrounded him.

111

21. Wheelchair Boy

Every night at about eight o'clock Sarah would wheel Karl's chair into his bedroom. She placed the chair in front of his computer screen and switched it on. Then she would transfer the control box to the tray on his chair. He was no longer capable of using a mouse. The box allowed him to access the whole keyboard with a limited range of hand movements and recently they had bought a voice-activated programme that typed the words he spoke. It still had some problems and he had not been able to abandon the manual box completely, but it had made the typing of words much easier.

Karl liked to enter chat rooms and talk to people. He was not alone in this as many disabled people have found computers to be a source of activity undreamed of previously. But one day he entered and simply said "I've got muscular dystrophy". To his surprise, someone replied and said "So have I. Give us you email address."

From then on the two boys had corresponded privately away from the chat room and although Karl still visited the chat room, these conversations were private. More significantly, the two never swapped personal details like addresses or telephone numbers.

His friend used the online name of 'Wheelchair Boy'. He was the only person whom he could talk freely to. There were other people in the same situation at school and college, but there was very little time to sit and just talk, and nowhere at all to talk privately. Now he had found a place where he could speak without inhibitions to someone who would understand. It was their world that no one else could enter. In the real world he was constantly surrounded by people who were meeting his every need except one; the need for privacy.

Here in his computer world he had his own thoughts and feelings expressed like never before to someone whom he had never seen and with whom he would not get too personally involved. They spoke about everything and anything. They talked about football. Karl liked Manchester United while Wheelchair Boy was a Newcastle United fan. He went to home games regularly. He once told Karl about the time he had spent a day with the stars at the club.

In turn Karl had told him about Castleton. Wheelchair Boy knew about rugby league, but as it wasn't played much in his area he hadn't paid too much attention. That had changed over the last 12 months as he had begun to watch it on television. They often spoke about games and he looked out for the Castleton matches. Often Karl would have to explain details about rules but over time Wheelchair Boy's' knowledge had increased and their conversations had become more involved.

They'd also spoken about girls, which female pop stars they fancied and who they were in love with. They also talked about girls they knew. If someone else had read these conversations they would not have gathered that any problems existed in this area. They were normal, teenage boys' conversations. Only occasionally was there a hint that there may be difficulties with girls and only once had there been a clear indication of real sexual frustration. Once Wheelchair Boy had talked about a girl at college that he liked and who talked to him a lot. He'd talked about her long light brown hair that rested on her neck and fell on a pair of fantastic tits. He talked about her sitting with him at dinner time and that he wanted to ask her out, but was too afraid.

He'd written a poem which he'd called "I love you but just as a friend" which he had refused to type for Karl out of embarrassment, but it showed a fear that "No-one would want to go out with the likes of us". Karl had tried to persuade him to ask her, but he had not managed to do so.

Karl typed "Hello"

"Hello"

This simple greeting was always immensely significant to the two boys. In this space they seemed to lose their inhibitions and fears. Here the unspoken words could be spoken.

Here they did not have to be brave for their mothers or polite to care assistants. Here they could tell the truth, sure in the fact that not only would the other person understand, but that there would be no comeback. If the conversation got too upsetting they could turn off without letting the other see their pain and the other person would always understand.

One conversation had simply run: "I've got something to tell you."

"What?"

"I'm going to die."

The cursor pulsed.

"When?"

"Soon."

"Me too. Who do you think will go first?"

"How old are you?"

"17."

"I'm 19. That's old."

Karl was taken aback by this. Of course he knew what was wrong with him. Of course, he knew he was going to die, but he'd tried not to think about it. Occasionally a little gremlin prodded him in the back and reminded him. He'd always been able to make them disappear, but this simple statement from Wheelchair Boy, made him stop.

"That's old."

Nineteen wasn't that far away. It meant that he hadn't got much time left. For the first time he felt fear. What was dying like? Who could he ask? He felt a surge of adrenalin. He couldn't talk to his mum. She had enough to deal with.

"What's dying like?"

113

The letters raced across the screen.

"I don't know."

"Is there anyone to ask?"

"They're all dead. Ha, Ha."

"Ha, ha. What will you miss?"

"Does it matter?"

"I'll miss me mum. I'll miss the rugby. I'll miss the sound of the crowd and the smell of beef burgers."

There was a pause and the cursor blinked. It continued to blink.

"Hello?"

The cursor continued and Karl waited.

"I have to go," and with that Wheelchair Boy removed himself from the screen.

He didn't reply to Karl for four days by which time Karl had begun to fear that his comrade would not contact him again. Each night he would sit in front of the screen and sign in and wait. Finally Wheelchair Boy said, "Hello."

"Where have you been?"

"I've been thinking."

"What about?"

"Everything. I don't want to talk about dying anymore."

"Right. Good. What shall we talk about?"

"I dunno."

"Boring."

There was a pause, then Karl told him about meeting Chris and how he was going to play for Great Britain in October. For the next few weeks they talked about football, school, girls, this and that. They never repeated that conversation. They held conversations that any teenagers would hold and there was no hint of what was looming. This hour, from eight until nine, became the highlight of the day. It always provided Karl with something to talk about with his mother as she prepared him for bed. He would tell her all the things that Wheelchair Boy had done as she washed and toileted him and got him into bed.

He had given his friend a made up name so that his mother didn't think it was strange that he didn't know his name. Then one day he sat at the screen and typed in, "Hello."

He eagerly awaited a reply. There was nothing so while he waited he read his messages. There was one from Wheelchair Boy. It said simply "Gone to hospital. See ya."

Karl thought no more about it. Perhaps he was just going for a check up and would be there the next day. But the next day came and went. As did the next, and the next, and the next, and the next. Each night he turned on the screen as hope was stealthily replaced by apprehension. Three weeks had gone by.

On the 26th day after that last message he sat and blinked at the screen as the computer fan hummed. He had no way of finding out. He had no idea of who Wheelchair Boy was or where he lived.

Then, he saw that death would come. He had known it. He had seen it when kids at school had died, but this was something different. This was his world where he could be himself, where he unmasked all his fears that he otherwise hid from view and suddenly, without warning, it had ceased to exist. He sat and stared at the screen once more willing a reply to appear but its reflection blinked in his glasses.

Silence. He sighed and switched off the computer. The screen went click and once more he was alone with his thoughts. He wouldn't try any more. Wheelchair Boy was gone. He was alone.

He sat there motionless. He felt a sadness he had never experienced before. Something special had gone. Something he couldn't explain, not even to his mother. In the semi-darkness he sat deep within himself. He did not hear his mother coming down the hall. He did not notice her come into the room nor did he sense her presence until she grabbed his shoulders and shouted softly "Boo!"

Her playful smile disappeared when she saw his face.

"Oh Karl, my love, what's wrong?"

He looked at his mother as tears filled his eyes and plummeted down his cheeks. He opened his mouth to speak and almost comically, saliva formed a bubble that popped as he gasped for air.

"Karl, what's the matter?" she cried as she saw the pain, the emptiness in his face and he cried into her chest. She stopped asking what was wrong. She just held him as tightly as she could. He was a big, grown up boy who was a fighter. He was her hero. She had always marvelled at his strength and fortitude, but all that had suddenly gone. He sobbed and she held him, gently calling his name.

It was then that she knew that something terrible had happened. Something she couldn't quite understand, but sensed and though neither of them said anything they nevertheless understood. Hope had been extinguished. The end had begun.

22. That was when he knew

The consequences of that night had been profound. Karl had stayed in bed for a whole week and refused to get up. It was the summer holidays and he did not need to get up to go to college. Normally, Karl not getting out of bed would have been a blessing in disguise for Sarah. She would have to look after his needs, but would not have to dress and undress him. This was different, however, because he had descended into a deep melancholy and she couldn't seem to rouse him from it. Sarah was worried.

Karl found himself motionless, unable rather than unwilling to move. Occasionally, he would glance over at the dead computer screen as if willing it to become active with a message from his friend, but no matter how often he tried, it did not respond.

He found himself thinking about things he hadn't thought about in years. Some of the things he thought about were memories he didn't know he'd lost. Some he couldn't recall happening at all, but there they were, in his head, so he didn't know whether they were real or imagined, but they felt real.

He remembered being able to walk, but at the same time it seemed that he'd been in the wheelchair for most of his life. His memory played tricks and distorted time as it does for children when they try to place things in a time frame.

Once he and his best friend Robert had met one of their television heroes in the centre of Castleton at a signing session for a book of poems he had written. He had been fantastic and had chatted to them both for a whole five minutes during a break from signing books and being nice to total strangers.

Karl had been surprised at how ordinary he was. He had no fancy ways. He was just a grown up with a smile. As proof of their meeting he had a signed photograph. He had written "Go Tiger! Best Wishes..." Karl had noted that he hadn't written his surname. That would have been something he did for everyone. This was personal. He looked funny. They had framed it and for the last three years it had been on the shelf in his room. Every time Karl looked at it he smiled.

The photograph was on the same shelf as another one. Chris Anderton was the kind of man he wanted to be. He was big, strong and could run fast. He was a bit like how he remembered his dad.

He used to go and watch his dad play rugby. Sometimes his mum would take him and sometimes grandad. He was so proud of his dad. Since he died he had thought about him every day and each time he would smile. He would talk about him to friends, to his mother, to anyone who would listen. Karl lay on his side and sighed. He missed his dad.

The photograph of Chris was him playing against Wigan. Karl had been at the game. He would point out to anyone who saw the photograph that he was in it. He would point to the crowd, just above Chris's right shoulder and slightly to the right. There he was – a blur in the out of focus distance. One little blob among 10,000 others, except that the area he was pointing to was the platform for people in wheelchairs. This amounted to proof that the blob was him. And if anyone doubted it, which no one did, he could recall details of the game. Castleton had won 18–15 with a try in the last minute. Karl would even produce the programme, because he kept all his programmes. The trouble was that he could no longer reach the shelves in the cupboards to fetch them down and read them. He had to rely on the others to do this for him. Melanie often sat with him and looked at them. She enjoyed rugby as much as he did. They would spend hours pouring over old photographs and club statistics. The photograph showed Chris being tackled by two Wigan players as he was looking to pass the ball to his right. Karl had positioned them like this on purpose. It seemed as if they were playing together in the same match, his two heroes, together, Chris passing the ball and the television star about to receive it, terrified at the prospect of being tackled. It looked so funny. Chris's picture also had writing on it: "To Mr Tough Guy. Kind regards Chris."

Karl was so pleased with that. Chris Anderton thought he was tough. Then he would feel great sadness. Why couldn't he be like the others? What had he done to deserve this? He had done nothing wrong. All he wanted to do was run around with his mates and have fun. Whenever he had these thoughts he made himself look at the photographs once more and smile. Look how lucky he was. He had friends like them. And Chris thought he was tough. He was a lucky boy. He would make himself look and smile. What was the point in being angry? What was the point? He was 17 and from somewhere he had plucked the courage and the fortitude to think like that. He truly was a tough guy.

His mind drifted. He visited times and places, some recent memories, some distant. Children are not stupid. Adults underestimate them. They know things. They understand. They remember.

He remembered a birthday party. It was a fine summer's day in June. He remembered a room. The sun shone through open French windows that led onto a lawn. He could smell all kinds of things: the food wafting in from the kitchen and mingling with the scent of flowers. He could hear birds singing and he had felt happy.

They played blind man's bluff and it was his turn. Older people put the blindfold on him and spun him round a couple of times. He remembered his senses wobbling a bit and he laughed. Everyone laughed, but as they laughed he felt a brief moment of uncertainty,

117

that things weren't quite right. Of course he wasn't able to put his finger on it because it was just a moment, and he'd never felt like that before. He'd never felt so... wobbly.

He had felt dizzy before but this was different. He remembered touching someone, a young woman. She took his hands and slipped them from her shoulder down her arms. He remembered the uncertain pleasure of her skin, warm and soft as she slid his hands down. He remembered smiling as she took off his blindfold so that he could confirm that his guess was correct. She was pretty and he thought that he loved her. He remembered that party. He could walk then. That was when he knew he was happy.

He remembered having a nice time in the park with his mum and when he thought about it he smiled, but then the smile always faded because he remembered falling over. It had been his second fall that day. He had sat on the floor rubbing his knee. He was annoyed, a feeling that increased 10-fold when he saw the remains of his ice cream on the footpath. This was daft. He'd never done this before. Then he saw his mother's face as she squatted down beside him and held his hand. He remembered her face. He remembered touching her cheek. For a brief moment his concern for his mother exceeded his concern for himself. He did not like to see her so afraid. That was when he knew something was wrong.

He had got used to needing other people as his condition worsened. Increasing dependency had been part of growing up. But as you grow up you become more aware. Until he was 14, nearly 15, he had looked to himself and his problems. He had not really thought about others; then one day he was in the corridor. It was a bright, sunny day. He was half dozing when he became aware of someone gently sobbing. It was Natasha. She was in the sixth form and he knew her from swimming lessons. She told him that Jamie had died in the night. He knew Jamie. He had muscular dystrophy like him.

People had died before, but they were always much older than him. Jamie was only three years older and he knew him well. They had travelled on the same bus for the past four years. He knew he had been away for a while, but had not thought much about it. People regularly went off for special treatment and they always came back.

He sat there in the corridor and an awful realisation came over him. When he got home he followed his mother into the kitchen and watched as she poured him a drink. He said "Mum?"

"Yes?"

"Am I going to die soon?"

His mother wheeled round in shock. He had asked this before, but she had managed to smooth over it, but his brutal suddenness caught her off guard. She could not disguise her feelings. He remembered her face. That was when he knew he was going to die.

118

23. Special needs

Karl was no fool. He knew he placed demands on others. He was aware of the disruption he caused.

For the last two or three years going to the toilet had become a problem. He simply couldn't decide to go as and when required. Toileting was a matter of planning. His teachers' aides were very kind, but no matter how discreet they were, everyone knew his business.

He disrupted lessons, as his big wheelchair had to be skilfully manoeuvred out of the classroom. He sat as near to the door as possible to avoid disturbing others, but he still had to inform staff and students of his needs. He wished he could go to the toilet without having to announce it to everyone. It wasn't much to ask.

Feeding had become another issue. Mum now fed him and then she ate her meal. They no longer ate together as such.

He always needed to be accompanied. He no longer had any privacy at all except when alone in his bed and even then his mum had to come to him every hour to turn him in order to avoid bed sores.

Of course, no one else saw him as a problem. The staff were wonderful. His family never ever complained, but he knew. All family life centred around his needs and while there was no question that this was the way things had to be, he always felt guilty that other people's needs came after his, but what could he do?

He hadn't chosen this, but still he was aware that other people had lives to lead. It wasn't his fault. He was innocent, but he couldn't help feeling guilty.

Sometimes he wanted to die.

Sometimes he wanted to live.

Most of the time he didn't know what he wanted.

He knew he wanted it to stop.

It was clear that Karl needed help.

How do you express how frightened you are of your own death? At 17 you don't deal with life all that well let alone death. More importantly, how do you tell your mother about your fears?

She has so much to do. You can't burden her any more. You already feel guilty. You know how much you make demands on her. You know how much you shape and limit other peoples' lives around you. You feel physically bad enough as it is without feeling guilty all the time, but what can you do? This is the hand you've been dealt and it's not your fault.

But how do you say that? You should be worrying about exams, your football team, whether girls like you, not death. How do you talk about that?

They have counsellors at school. What do you say? You say nothing. You tell them you're Okay and put it to the back of your mind. It's not going to happen.

You're frightened for yourself, but there's another reason you stay silent. You're frightened for her. You look at your mum in a different way to other teenagers. You don't know that you do, but you do.

You notice the tiredness in her eyes. You watch the top of her head when she bends down to straighten your bedding. You see the sadness behind her smile and you know she misses dad. She has enough to cope with so you don't bother her with your fears. How do you tell your mum that your biggest fear is not about dying itself, although that really does scare the shit out of you? Your biggest worry is about how she'll cope when you're gone. She misses dad and you don't want to make her miss you so you say nothing.

You feel so alone so you smile and push your fear to the back of your mind. The back of your mind is a very convenient place.

Karl was not he only one whose life was changed by that evening. It was obvious that things could not continue as they had. Karl had reached a crisis, but so had Sarah. She knew that she had to do something, but had no idea what it was.

Sarah knew that Karl loved his computer, but since she had stopped seeing Chris, she had noticed that he had been spending more time on it. It was as if he had withdrawn from her, or maybe not from her but into himself. He didn't seem as keen to talk to or even be with other people. Sarah had already begun to worry about him, but Karl's loss of his friend made things even worse. It showed that she had no idea of what he was really thinking. She did not know what to do next.

It had always been in the back of her mind to talk to Karl about his feelings, but the back of the mind can be a very convenient place.

Karl had not moved for a week, exhausted by his emotional experience. Sarah sat watching the television but she was so preoccupied she didn't know what the programme had been about. She turned it off so that she could listen to herself think.

It was at times like this when she could have done with some company. If the truth were known she could have done with someone to hold her, to make her feel that someone was protecting her. Every night she thought of her husband. The thoughts comforted her. They reminded her of good times, but the pleasure was always temporary and broken by reality. It began to dawn on her that thinking of Dave was not a practical solution to her problems. Dave was gone. It was as simple as that and she cuddled the cushion in her loneliness.

Everyone thought she coped so well, but she knew she didn't. Her dreams told her that. Sarah knew that she merely existed. She had no-one to talk to about her deepest fears. She couldn't talk to her mother. She didn't want to burden her because she was not unaffected by this. Her children were too young and too scared and anyway, she was the adult. She had to care for them. She could have talked to Karl, but how do you speak to a 17 year old about his imminent death and how he feels about it, how you feel about it?

How would you expect him to feel?

She knew he wouldn't talk about it anyway. So if he didn't talk about it she couldn't. She had to wait, to be there when he needed her. Yet she had needs and her words remained unspoken.

They were two people, so desperately needing to talk; so unable to do so; shrouded in silence.

24. In the night

Karl's bedroom was adjacent to his mother's. This was a sensible arrangement. Every night she moves from her room to his on at least 10 occasions. Being next door means she has a shorter distance to move in the middle of the night.

She controls the space between their rooms. Nothing is left on the floor. No bags, magazines, clothes, are left to trip over. No Hoovers, no trailing flex from lamps, nothing is ever left. The physical channels are always clear. Everything is checked and double-checked every night.

After she has tended to his needs she can find her way back on automatic pilot without the risk of falling over something. She doesn't even have to open her eyes.

It is also sensible because although her sleep is disturbed on a regular, known basis, it also means that she can hear him should he cry out for anything else.

Karl's bed stands along the wall that divides their bedrooms. It is a large room and the bed could have easily been placed in the middle, allowing nursing access from both sides, but that would have simply doubled the chance of Karl's falling out. Sarah is terrified that should this happen she would be unable to lift Karl back into the bed. More recently she has become concerned that, in his weakening condition, such a fall would result in a broken bone or bones.

The fact that Karl has never called out for his mother at an unscheduled time and has never fallen out of bed and injured himself, in any way, is irrelevant. She lives a life of 'might be'. It is a life of stress, of fear. She is forever watchful, thinking, frightened and above all, she is tired. She is completely exhausted.

Her bed is situated in the middle of her room. Each night their doors are open. She can hear her son and he knows she is watchful. Their lives are connected and intertwined. Even in her sleep she watches over him.

Karl had still not got out of bed. Sarah decided that she would have to confront him. He had to come out of his depression or he would die.
She lay awake. She glanced at the clock that said 2.55am. Its red light flickered as it moved to 2.56am. She lay there, waiting. 2.57am.

Every night she did this, at every hour. She had not known an undisturbed night since the previous March, almost 16 months ago when Karl had endured a week's respite care in a Rest Home. Karl hated it, but Sarah needed it desperately. She had slept for nearly 24 hours on the first day and then just when she had felt her strength return she had immediately begun to feel guilty; guilty that she wasn't looking after him; guilty that she had enjoyed a decent sleep. She had been so tired. Her mum had said all the right things. She knew that she wasn't a bad mother, that the rest would allow her to care for longer but rational thought didn't help in an emotional situation. She had slept poorly after that first day, worrying about how he felt. Now, she lay there once more, too tired to sleep.

The clock blinked.

2.58am.

She heard a car go by and wondered why anyone else would be moving about at this time of the morning. They wouldn't be going to work. Shifts didn't change at this time of the night. Perhaps it was a robber making his getaway or someone on a mercy mission taking someone who was poorly to hospital. On a more positive note, it might have been a young husband taking his wife to hospital to give birth. She hoped it was the latter. People shouldn't have to be awake at this time unless there was some reward. She remembered her own births vividly. She remembered Melanie's arrival. That had been in the early hours. She could see Dave dashing about, putting things in the car, telling her she'd be okay.

She sighed.

Soon, in two minutes precisely, in fact, she would get up, go to Karl's room and turn him over into a new position. She had done this now for... she couldn't remember how long. It must have been nearly two years since his muscles had degenerated to such an extent that he could no longer move himself. Lying in the same place for a long period would create pressure sores that could easily become infected and he had to be turned regularly to avoid this.

The clock blinked.

2.59am.

Sometimes she would shuffle in, do what was required and stumble back to sleep with just the briefest of kisses. Sometimes, there were moments when they would talk, softly about anything, but often it was about something that had happened at college. Occasionally, less often, she would be the one doing the talking, usually about how much she loved him and how proud she was of him. She would turn him and make him comfortable. Then she would stroke his forehead with the back of her hand and then her palm. She would hold his hand and kiss him before returning to her bed with a "Night, night". He was 17, but it was still, "Night, night". The phrase was comfortable and secure, continued from his childhood. It was special. It was theirs and he had never once asked her to stop it and replace it with something more grown up.

3am.

The buzzer sounded just as she had nodded off again. She gasped awake and was out of bed in the same movement. Her feet fumbled for her slippers in the dark while she slipped on her dressing gown. She left her room and yawned her way onto the hallway that was lit dimly by the soft light coming from Karl's bedroom. He had always had the light on ever since he was a baby.

Her mother had bought her a nursing lamp when he was born. It was a beautiful bedside lamp in the form of a white ceramic boot with a roof on top. A gentle yellow restful light sprinkled in every direction, without brightening the room too much.

Once she had decided that Karl was too old for such a lamp, but he had insisted on keeping it and had never since asked for it to be removed. He was comforted by things familiar and there was a peace in this room despite the troubles that lived within it.

Sarah smiled at her son, but did not speak. Karl looked at his mum. He could see the tiredness in her eyes and he wished things were different. He didn't want his mum to have to struggle, but he had long since resigned himself to the situation he found himself in. He was too weak and tired to do anything about it, but he so wished it were different. As she bounced him over he grunted. Such movements were necessary, but they were starting to hurt. He hadn't told his mum because he didn't want her to worry any more than she already did. He knew she had too much to do and that moving him was a big effort for her, but that knowledge didn't reduce his pain. He grunted once more and when she asked him if he was comfy he lied, like he had lied every night for the past month. The truth was he no longer believed that he *could* get comfortable, but to tell his mum would make her realise that things were getting worse and he didn't want her to worry any more than she already did. So he lied. Every night he lied and every night he smiled when she asked him if he was comfy and every night she would say "Night, night" and he would reply, "Night, night".

As she slipped into the darkness and towards a grateful sleep his smile would fade, however, as he felt the loneliness of a night, with little comfort, begin to wrap itself around him.

He would lie there and listen to his clock tick. He liked clocks and his mum had bought him several. His favourite was the one in the wooden box which was mounted on the wall in the dining room. He could hear the sound of its gentle chiming drift down the passageway towards him. In his bedroom his clock was a simple Mickey Mouse wind up, but he liked the noise it made. Often it would send him to sleep during a difficult night. The only trouble was the nights were becoming more and more difficult.

"Are you comfy love?"

"Yes mum" he lied once more.

"Do you want anything else?"

"A new body would help."

"Mmm, well I'm afraid I can do most things but not that."

They smiled quietly at each other and then Karl said "Mum, I'm not a wheelchair boy. I'm a boy in a wheelchair, aren't I?"

"What do you think?"

"Yes, I'm a boy in a wheelchair. You don't call people in cars a car man or a woman car do you? They are people who use cars and I'm a boy who uses a wheelchair."

"Yes. Quite right. Why do you ask?"

"The boy I used to speak to on my computer. He called himself Wheelchair Boy. I just knew I didn't like being called a wheelchair boy as if I was part of one. I'm not. I'm me. That's who I am. I should have told him. I'm sick of being labelled as disabled. I'm me aren't I?"

Sarah smiled proudly at her son.

"Oh you're you alright." She ruffled his hair and smiled and then despite himself Karl asked her a question he had never meant to ask her. It was a question that was always on his mind, but never on his lips. He had always managed to keep the question in one place and then suddenly, unpredictably and unintentionally the question moved and he asked it before he could stop it.

"Mum?"

"Yes?"

"When I die..."

The force of the words knocked the breath out her and she tried not to show distress. Instinctively she took hold of his right hand.

"Yes?" She said almost silently.

"Will you miss me?"

Sarah wrestled with her thoughts. Should she answer or should she discourage this conversation?

She answered. Holding back tears and squeezing his hand tighter than she meant to she said "What do you think?"

"That's a cheat. I asked you."

They smiled as she whispered "Of course I won't. I'm going to go out clubbing every night and have a ball."

He smiled. "Good. I think you ought to. You deserve it."

And she smiled again and marvelled at his kindness. He was so young and he looked so vulnerable in the half-light and she so wanted to hold him tight and squeeze him, but she knew that such affection would hurt him too much so she did what she always did when she wanted to show him her love. She held his hand, stroked his forehead and then he said "If you had your time again..."

And she so wanted to stop him saying the next words, but they came anyway and she choked as if an arrow had been fired through her throat so that she couldn't swallow or speak.

"Would you still have me?"

And her chest heaved and her head nodded vigorously as if to shake the arrow out and she said "I love you with all my heart. I love you so very....very ...much... Never...ever.... think that I am not glad that I had you..... I love you. Knowing you is a joy. Do you hear me?" And she stroked his head over and over again. "You are so brave, so tough so selfless and you have given me, taught me, so much."

"Am I as tough as a rugby league player?"

"What rugby league player could deal with what you deal with? The other day Chris was talking about how much he admired you."

"Really?"

"Yeah, of course he does. You're the bravest, toughest of them all, my lad. The bravest of them all and I have never questioned having you. We were frightened when the doctors first told us, but you have brought so much to me."

She paused, wondering what else to say, but unable to think of anything. "Does that answer your question?"

"Yeah" he said quietly. "I'm sorry for asking, but I had to know."

"Yes. I know."

Then he fired another arrow.

"Mum?"

"Yes?"

"Why have you stopped seeing Chris?"

She paused. They hadn't actually stopped seeing each other. They hadn't said anything to each other that would end the relationship. It was just that life seemed to be getting in the way. She just couldn't seem to find the time or the energy. So they hadn't stopped seeing each other, they just hadn't seen each other.

After a week or so she had begun to doubt whether he wanted to continue. He hadn't phoned. She was dimly aware that she wanted him to 'pursue' her, but hadn't got time for him when he did and yet was disappointed when he didn't. She didn't know what she wanted. It was all too much but at the same time she didn't want to lose him.

"He misses you."

"How do you know? Has he told you?"

"No. I just know."

"Mum? Have you split up because of me?"

Sarah tried to say no.

"If it is then I don't want that. You should be happy mum. Don't waste your life. Do you want to be on your own?"

"No, but..."

"Well then. One day soon..." There was a very slight pause. "I won't be here. You have to think about you."

Sarah could say nothing. She kept stroking his head while trying to hold back the tears that were beginning to flood down her cheeks.

Then she stood up wiped her face with her nightdress so that he wouldn't know she'd been crying, leant over and kissed him. She stroked his forehead with the back of her hand and then her palm and

126

held his hand for a brief moment. She moved to the door and before leaving turned to look at him and whispered,

"Night, night."

"Night, night." he replied.

"Mum."

"Yes?"

"Life's too short."

She felt dizzy and grabbed the door frame for support.

"I know."

She paused.

"Thank you."

"S' alright."

"You're a clever lad."

"Night, night."

And with that she returned to her bed and he to his darkness. Only this time the darkness quickly left him as he slipped into a deep and restful sleep.

It was 3.21am.

25. Reunited

Sarah also had some good rest for the first time in years if you discount the constant rising to turn Karl. She was pleased. The conversation had been as unexpected as it was welcome. Karl had cleared the air and in doing so had not only made life easier for his mother, but had also lifted himself out of his depression.

Next morning he was bright and cheerful once more. At the breakfast table he asked Sarah a simple question.

"Mum?"

"Why do I suspect something difficult is coming?"

Karl smiled. "It's not difficult, honest."

"What then?"

"Can I have a party?"

"What for?"

"Just to say, well, thanks to people."

"Thanks?"

"Yeah, you know to my friends, before it's too late."

Sarah was pleased that they were both able to talk about their feelings, but she realised, with that one sentence, that openness and honesty might have a down side. Karl was preparing to say goodbye. It was obvious that he had thought about the end and was already preparing for it.

Sarah continued to pour out the breakfast cereal.

"Well, yes, if you really feel it is necessary."

She spoke quietly and softly. She looked directly at Karl who gained in confidence. "Yes, I've been thinking about it. I want to see people, everybody."

"Okay."

"Including Chris."

This was a statement, it wasn't a question. Sarah knew that she couldn't refuse. It was what he wanted and she would have to deal with it.

"When?" She asked in a matter of fact way.

"Next week."

Sarah convinced Karl that that would be too quick. People would need more warning and she would need time to get things ready so they compromised on a fortnight.

Sarah divided the task of phoning people between herself, Melanie and James. Karl would invite his college friends, but she left the job of inviting Chris to herself.

She rang him in the evening when she had put Karl to bed.

"Hello."

Sarah was surprised how nervous she was.

"H... Hello," she stuttered.

"Sarah?"

"Yes," she said breathily.

There was a silence.

"Hello?"

"Oh, I was wondering or, or rather Karl was wondering. Well we were both wondering actually..."

She sounded like Bridget Jones, struggling to think of the right words. She could hear Chris listening patiently, trying to work out what the hell she was saying.

"We wanted to know if you'd like to come to a party?"

"Sure, no problem."

She smiled, as she always did when he used that phrase. "Would you like to know when the problem, I mean party is?"

If he noticed her slip, he didn't show it.

"It's a week on Saturday."

"Yes, I can make that. What's it for?"

She took a deep breath and her nervousness was replaced by seriousness. "Karl has decided he would like to see everyone."

"I see." There was a pause. "It must be very hard for you."

In that one instance of kindness she dissolved. "It won't be much longer."

"No. I know."

"He, I mean, we just wanted to see." Her voice tailed off and she could not manage the word 'you'.

"I'll be there. You can rely on me."

"I know I can," she said weepily, "Look. I'm sorry".

"It's okay."

"Everything." Her throat was dry. "Everything. Very hard."

"I know." They were both speaking very softly.

"Would you like me to come round?"

She nodded heavily without speaking. She coughed.

"That would be nice."

"I'm on my way," and he put the phone down leaving her hanging onto the silence. Her hair fell around her face as she sat there, head bowed. Before she realised it there was a knock on the door. She stumbled down the hall and opened the door. He stood there, filling the entrance. Without speaking, she burst into tears and collapsed into his arms.

"I feel so confused," she sobbed. "I'm waiting for my son to die."

"Shhhh. It's okay," he said softly.

"No, but it's not. I was so afraid I'd lose you that I couldn't bear the worry. I couldn't worry about anything else so I sent you away."

"I know. It's all right, really."

"I don't want to lose you."

"You won't, I promise."

129

"I feel so guilty, waiting for him to die so that I can be with you."

Chris took hold of both her hands and looked straight into her eyes.

"Now listen to me. You mustn't think like that. None of this is your fault. It's no one's fault. Do you hear me?" She nodded through her tears. "You deserve happiness. It's not your fault. Are you listening?" Again she nodded. "I'm not waiting for Karl to die and do you know what? Neither is he. We can do this together, you, me, all of us. The time we've got left." He paused at the sound of those words. "We'll make them happy ones. Okay?"

"I'm so tired."

"I know you are."

She rested her head against his chest. Without a word he picked her up. She felt so light and frail that he wondered where her strength came from.

He carried her to her bedroom and laid her on the bed. She was already fast asleep. She did not stir when he slipped her skirt and blouse off. He leant over her, gently kissed her on the cheek and said, "You deserve happiness my love."

The words surprised him. He had never said that he loved her. In fact, until this moment he hadn't known that he did. He stood there listening to her sleep. He walked round the other side of the bed and undressed. He watched her breathing and smiled to himself as he settled down beside her. Together, they slept.

In the early hours of the morning, Sarah returned to bed after attending Karl. Without any sense of surprise she snuggled her back into Chris as if it were the natural thing to do.

26. Preparations

Sarah enjoyed that week and the next, preparing for the party. Chris had been great, but the demands on his time meant that he had only slept over once. He needed to be at his physical best and disturbed nights interfered with that. It was also true that as much as she enjoyed his presence, she could not get used to the idea of someone else being there when she dealt with Karl. She was living in a special world that required her to calculate everything she did. Sarah had to balance normality against abnormality, private lives and shared lives. She had to make choices between people who all made demands on her time and being. This was more tiring than the continuous loss of sleep that ate into her. Every time she wished for rest she was reminded of the fact that her wish would be granted sooner rather than later.

She had originally suggested to Karl that they hire somewhere for the party, but he was desperate to have it at home. On reflection Sarah agreed it was probably the best idea. If Karl needed anything he was better at home. Travelling had become an issue because it tired him. He had not gone to choir with his grandad for over three weeks and the prospects of him returning to college were diminishing. So the party was to be held at home.

"It will be cramped, especially, with several wheelchairs present." She was concerned about the arrangements, but as Karl darkly pointed out: "It'll be just as cramped as it will be at the funeral."

Sarah had to admit that he had a point. She didn't know whether she liked this form of humour that he had developed, but she reasoned that at least it meant that he was in a positive frame of mind. Then he added, "Well, not quite as cramped. There'll be one chair less." Sarah and Mel exchanged glances, but Karl was too busy laughing at his macabre joke to notice. Sarah was anxious to ensure that Karl kept his strength without upsetting his brother and sister. She couldn't reprimand him, but she had become increasingly aware of the strain they were under.

Mel turned silently, kissed her brother on the head and walked quickly out. Karl probably sensed that he had gone too far. The five minute silence was deafening.

"I just want to be happy."

"Well, we want you to. It's not easy for Mel and James, but they'll manage. Anyway, I've got to carry on baking these scones." With that she turned back to her task and made a mental note to talk to Mel, to both of them. She wouldn't do it now. Mel was probably in her room crying. She left it, but thought that she would have to speak to them before the party.

Sarah sighed. She was trying to manage the impossible. She was trying to make sure that everyone was happy or at least able to deal with the situation.

It was also obvious to her that the one person whose needs she wasn't managing properly were her own. She was grateful to Chris, she really was. He did everything she asked, but doubt was nagging at her again. As kind as he was the fact was that she wasn't free. Monday hadn't been a mistake. It had been lovely and yet...

"You'll smash those currants to a pulp if you're not careful."

"Are you alright?"

"Yes, of course."

Sarah looked down. The table was covered in flour.

"Yes, I'm fine. I'll finish this later. It's getting late. Time for bed young man."

"Do I have to?"

"I'm afraid you do. I'm knackered."

Half an hour later, Sarah was sat on the edge of her son's bed having washed and changed him.

"Do you know one thing I would wish for if I had the chance?"

"What?"

"I'd like to go to bed by myself when I decide to."

"I know. I'm sorry, but I really am tired."

"It's not your fault. It's just a bit of a bugger that's all."

Suddenly her earlier anxiety disappeared. She was worrying about the way in which Karl's attitude was affecting others and all he wanted was to go to bed by himself. No wonder she had recently noticed that he had developed an edge.

She smiled at him in that helpless manner she had developed. She was right to protect Mel and James's feelings, but she had to protect Karl as well. She was trapped between competing needs and there was no way to resolve the dilemma. Her mind whirled under the pressure. Sarah did not want him to see her pain, nor did she want Mel and James to notice it either, so she smiled. She always smiled.

"Night, night."

"Night, night mum."

She turned in the doorway and whispered, "See you in the morning." But the boy who had not wanted to go to bed was already fast asleep.

She had not planned to do it yet. In fact she hadn't been certain whether she was going to do it at all, but that sentence "I wish I could go to bed by myself" had decided it. She had to speak to the others.

She popped her head round Mel's door. She was lying on her bed reading a magazine. Her eyes were red and it was obvious that she was upset.

132

"Have you got a minute? I need to talk to you and James together."

Mel nodded without speaking. She knew from her mother's tone what it was about. She closed the magazine and left her room. Her mother was leaning into James's room. As she straightened up they nearly collided.

"Whoops." Sarah smiled. They walked into the lounge. Sarah turned off the television and motioned to them to sit down. Mel knew what this was about while James, unaware of the previous conversation looked at his mother enquiringly.

"I need to talk to you both."

"What about?"

"Karl," said Mel, anxious to help her mother.

"Oh." James's simple word summed up the gravity of the situation. They knew what their mother was going to say the unsaid. No one had talked about it, perhaps hoping that the situation would never arise but, here they were. It was time.

"You need to know that things are getting serious." Sarah hesitated, looking at them. Softly she said, "We've not got long." For a moment there was still no response.

"How long?" James asked, wanting some certainty.

"I don't know. Not long. Weeks," and then she hesitated, almost imperceptibly, "Maybe less."

"Will he make it to the World Cup?"

It seemed such an irrelevant question. Certainly, Sarah had never given it a moment's thought, yet it was the most important question of all. Karl had been looking forward to watching Chris for nearly a year. Probably his main motivation for living would begin in just under a month. Sarah caught her breath. Words like 'soon,' and 'not long' seemed to suggest urgency, but they were just words. Seeing the World Cup as part of the timescale brought the idea of 'soon' into sharp focus. 'Soon' was a month.

"I think so," she said weakly, trying to convince herself as well as her children. "Yes, he will. I'm certain."

"It's not long."

"No."

There was a silence as they all took in this conversation.

"I just wanted to say that I love you. Really, that's all."

"I love you too." Both of them spoke softly and in unison.

"Karl can be a bit awkward sometimes but he's got reason. We're just going to have to be strong and put up with it. We need to stick together, don't we?"

They nodded, again in unison. They found themselves together in a huddle on the settee. James laid his head on his mother's lap and she stroked his hair. Mel rested her head on Sarah's breast. They lay there for an age without speaking. Each had their own thoughts, but all were about the young man in the bedroom down the hall. Unspoken, one thought crept in to their minds for the first time, clear and stark.

Karl was dying.

Eventually James got up and walked wearily off to bed. Sarah watched him fumble with the door.

Mel sat up. "Are you okay mum?

"Mmm? Yes, why?"

She had been momentarily lost in her thoughts, reflecting on the implications of their earlier conversation and the question had surprised her. "Yes. I'm okay." She smiled as convincingly as she could at her daughter's kind face. 'My children are so grown up,' Sarah thought to herself. She had been concerned about their welfare, but the conversation had turned to an enquiry about hers.

"Are you sure?"

"Yes, yes," she lied. "Yes I'm fine. Honestly I am."

"You don't look it."

"Oh, thanks very much," she smiled.

"You know what I mean. You look tired mum and you never cry."

"There's no point in crying. I've got too much to do anyway." She stroked her daughter's hair.

"You never moan either. You always seem like you're dealing with things, everything."

"Do you want me to start moaning?"

"No. You know what I mean."

"I suppose I haven't thought about it. I suppose..."

She stopped in mid-sentence. "I suppose I'll have time to moan..."

"When Karl dies?"

Sarah looked into Mel's eyes. "After Karl dies ... I suppose ... Yes." Sarah re-gathered herself. "I'm not going to not deal with this. I mean I am going to deal with this. I'm not going to let Karl worry. He's got enough to deal with. We must be strong. That's all there is."

Mel nodded and embraced her mother. "I love you mum, but just remember, James and I, we're in this as well and we know what the score is. We're not kids."

"Right."

"If ever you need..."

"I know. Thanks." She got up to go to bed.

"Night."

"Night, night."

Sarah went into the kitchen. She tidied up, trying not to think, but the more she tried not to, the more she thought. She went to bed and lay there before drifting into a fitful and restless sleep.

27. Sarah's dream

Sarah was sitting on her ledge. It was her ledge now, not 'the' ledge. 'Possession is nine tenths of the law' and no one else was seeking to claim it from her. She became aware that a light was emerging from the darkness and flooding her ledge. Her ledge resembled a minimalist stage without props of any kind, just a bare set backed by thick black curtains. Sarah peered into the darkness, but was blinded by the light.

"Read the charge."

A voice boomed and echoed around the stage.

"You are charged with crimes against your loved ones."

"I have committed no crime!"

"Silence." The voice was overpowering. "The charges are as follows: You gave birth to a disabled child and caused him pain. True or false?"

"I didn't know."

"True or false?"

"True but..."

"You have directed anger at your husband because he left you alone."

"Only when I was tired. I miss him so."

"Answer the question!"

"True. I'm sorry."

"You have wished that your son had never been born."

"No!"

"You lie!"

"I never meant it. I just wanted it all to stop. Please help me!"

"True or false?"

"True. True, true! You know it's true. Why do you ask?"

"Because you have to be punished!"

Sarah was sobbing uncontrollably.

"You have sought pleasure in the arms of another."

"Yes". She whispered thinly through her tears. "What was I supposed to do?

"You have wished for your son's death."

Silence. Sarah did not reply. Her head was bowed. Her hair, damp from her tears, lay about her face. She was bedraggled.

"How do you plead?"

"Not guilty." Her voice had become even thinner.

"Speak up!"

"Not guilty!"

"Sarah Burgess, you have been found guilty by this court. The sentence is that you remain here, alone forever"

"Please help me. I don't know what to do. Help me! I beg you!"

Sarah cried out, but the lights faded and the others disappeared. She was left alone in silence and blackness, sitting on her ledge.

Sarah woke with a start as she does each time she has her dream. The pyjamas, wet with sweat, were also a regular feature.

'No wonder I never put weight on.' She mocked herself and her dream. It frightened her, yet she has learnt to deal with it. It is something that happens.

She sniffed and ran her hand through her hair, trying to gather her wits. She had been sat up for a minute, but only now did she become aware that the alarm was beeping. She stared at the clock in disbelief. It was two hours since she last attended to Karl. She had never missed her duty, never. Now the failed mother of her dream stumbled in panic towards the son she had neglected in reality. It was a confirmation of her inadequacy. In her haste she stubbed her toe on the foot of the bed and cried out in pain. She hopped and half stumbled towards Karl's bedroom. Despite her rush she still managed to turn his bony body with some gentleness and whisper, "Night, night."

Karl replied in kind, but did not wake up as Sarah limped back to her room. She fell, exhausted, on top of the duvet. She clutched her foot and cried herself to sleep.

She woke the next morning with a mild ache in her foot. It was sore, but she was certain that it wasn't broken. In fact she hadn't thought about it on the five occasions she had fallen out of bed to see to Karl. 'That's nothing unusual,' she thought to herself. 'I never notice anything in the middle of the night at the best of times.'

She moved gingerly towards Karl's bedroom. As she became more awake she could certainly feel it. 'I didn't half give myself a bang,' she thought to herself as she pushed the door open.

Any thoughts of her own pain disappeared immediately at the sight of her son. Somehow Karl was twisted at an angle to the bed head, his face pressed awkwardly against the guardrails which stopped him from falling out She always left him in the middle of the bed, safe and secure. Her mind raced. How could he have moved?

"Karl? Karl love, wake up. Karl!"

She touched him. He was warm.

"Karl, love wake up."

It took five minutes before Karl responded. Sarah had been genuinely frightened. He normally woke up quickly, but he had been in a deep sleep and was very groggy. Neither of them could explain how he had got into that position. The only thing Sarah could think of was that, in his sleep, he had made a mighty effort to move, for some reason and that effort had exhausted him. The question was what had made him want to move?

Sarah did not like it. The desire to hold a thank you, or farewell party, followed by a serious event in his sleep; this was not good. Though he might protest otherwise, something was bothering Karl. Boys in the late stages of muscular dystrophy didn't move themselves. It was as simple as that. Something was happening to Karl. Sarah was confused and frightened. On the one hand she wanted to know what it was. On the other, she was afraid of what she might find out.

28. The end

The party was a great success. People started arriving at about 4pm because Karl's weakened state usually left him exhausted by 8pm.

Chris arrived at 7pm. Sarah had begun to worry that he had forgotten and was beginning to feel the first twinges of annoyance when in he came with Sean Wood, the Castleton and Great Britain stand-off. He was Karl's second favourite player to Chris. When she saw Karl's face light up, Sarah immediately forgave him and she became further enamoured when the two of them presented him with tickets for the World Cup Final.

"Oh bloody hell! Bloody hell!" exclaimed Karl. His eyes turned in delight to his mother as his neck was now too weak to turn his head. Chris had to place the tickets so that he could hold them with his fingers. He was not able to make a fist. She gently took them from him and placed them on the mantelpiece, slipping one end into the frame of Dave's picture.

"Don't leave 'em there mam, someone might nick 'em!"

"Well, they're not your real friends then."

"I'd steal 'em if I had to!"

Everyone laughed as Karl managed a weak grin at his own joke.

"And this is for you."

Chris turned to Sarah and pulled out a small jewellery box. She took it from him hesitantly and opened it, revealing a beautiful pendant and chain.

"Thank you," she said softly as she took it from the box. Chris helped to put it on and then she turned, put her arms around him and kissed him gently on the lips. It was her first public display of affection towards him. They stood there in the middle of the front room.

"Fuck me!"

"Language, young man." Sarah was surprised at herself. She had never felt so free in herself, nor so happy.

"My tickets are better than your necklace."

"Stuff your tickets."

"Oh you won't be saying that on Cup Final day." It was obvious that Karl's quick wit had not diminished as his body had.

The evening began to end as parents took their children home. Four specially adapted people carriers loaded up their passengers and took them slowly away. Karl sat there shouting his farewells as loudly as he could. By the time the last person left it was 9.30pm.

"Well I think that was a success," Sarah began to clear away the plates assisted by Mel and Chris.

"Mum."

"Yes, love?"

"I've got something for you." He glanced at Chris who produced a small box and placed it on the tray that was attached to Karl's chair.

"This is just to say thanks. I know you've worked so hard."

Silently she picked up the box and opened it. Inside was a ring with a stone to match the pendant. She slipped it on to the third finger of her right hand.

"Thank you. Thank you so very much, both of you."

Her voice was almost inaudible in its sincerity. She stood there, as her children and Chris watched her, holding her hand out, admiring her present. She smiled at them girlishly and turned to continue clearing up.

After putting Karl to bed they sat together in the front room. The evenings were drawing in quickly as September prepared to give way to October. They sat together holding hands occasionally kissing and smiling, but saying little. Sarah was tired, but relaxed, and more importantly, happy. Despite her misgivings things had gone really well. For the first time in a long time she did not feel that the entire world was on her shoulders. She had support, someone she could rely on. Maybe she was in love?

She felt at peace, but the peace would not last long.

On the Monday after the party Sarah went in to Karl's bedroom at 8am as she did every morning since he had not been at college. Normally he was already awake, but today he did not respond when she shouted "Good morning". Thinking he was probably tired after the weekend's excitement, Sarah decided not to open the curtains and left him to enjoy a lie in.

At 10am she crept round his door carrying a cup of tea.

"Karrrrl" she called playfully as she opened his curtains. "It's late".

Karl grunted feebly.

"Karl, are you alright?"

"Don't feel well." She could barely hear him.

Sarah put the cup down. He had seemed well and responsive the last time she had been in to turn him. A sudden deterioration in his condition alarmed her. She felt his forehead. It was burning.

"I'm going to call the doctor."

Sarah expected Karl to protest. He didn't. That confirmed it. He was really ill. She phoned the doctor and then she phoned her mum. It took no more than an hour for Doctor Fitzpatrick to call, examine Karl and call the ambulance. Within two hours he was being lifted off the stretcher and into bed in room 3, ward C2 at Castleton Hospital. He was the only occupant of this four-bedded room that was directly opposite the nursing station.

During all this time; the awkwardness of carrying him into the ambulance, the ambulance ride and the transfer from the stretcher to the bed, Karl had said nothing. Sarah and her mother stood in the corner as the nurses attached sensors to him and watched as the heart monitor began to register his weak pulse.

Finally the nurses left with a kindly smile.

"If you need anything just push this buzzer."

The women nodded in tandem.

"Would you like a cup of tea?"

"Yes, please," said June, looking at her daughter. "We could both do with a drink."

As the door shut Sarah took hold of her son's hand and kissed it.

"He looks so frail mum."

June sighed. "Yes he does love. He looks very tired poor lad."

"He doesn't deserve this. It's not fair," and she kissed his limp hand once more.

"No. It isn't fair. It never has been. I don't know what to say love."

"There isn't anything to say mum. There isn't anything to say." She kissed his hand again. "No-one can say anything."

The nurse entered. "The doctor's here to examine Karl. I've put you a cup of tea each in the day room. You can stay there while you wait." The two women exchanged gentle smiles with a young doctor as they left the room. They sat together in silence. Sarah stared into some imaginary distance. June sipped her tea.

"You need a drink, lass."

"Mmm."

"We're going to be here for a long time."

"Yeah. I know. We'd better tell people what's happening."

"I'll do it after the doctor's been."

"All that time. All that time knowing, waiting. Then suddenly before you know it..."

She stopped in mid-sentence afraid to say the next words that were on her lips. "He's not gone yet love. You know Karl, he's a fighter. He won't give up without a fight."

"Mum, he doesn't weigh five stone. He's got no strength to fight with. This is it. We have to face it."

June said nothing. There was nothing to say for in her heart she knew it was true. He was so weak and had become ill so quickly. How could he find the strength to fight back? Her daughter was right. After years of waiting, hoping, living life to the best possible, this was it. They sat there both hoping they were wrong as Sarah's tea went cold.

Half an hour went by and the two women hadn't said a word. Silence said everything and it deafened them both. June hadn't noticed it at first, but she could now hear the tiny ticking of the battery-operated clock on the wall to her left. She looked at the second hand moving jerkily round its face, then she watched it again, counting every second. Sarah changed her position. She stood up and went to the window. Below her was a courtyard containing slatted benches and two small trees. A nurse hurried from one end to the other. Two women, probably a mother and daughter, sat smoking and waiting for something. Sarah wondered who or what they were waiting for? Were they like her and her mother, waiting for something they didn't want to wait for?

She was aware that her mother needed to talk, even if it was just for the sake of it, but she hadn't got anything to say. She was empty. Sarah smiled at her. She had never failed her and she loved her dearly, but for now there was nothing. Her mother smiled back.

"They're taking a long time."

"Yes."

"They must be doing a thorough job."

Sarah nodded and turned back to observe the empty courtyard. Just then the door handle clicked and the lever moved downwards. Sarah watched it intently. Its movement was about to tell her something. There was a pause and she could hear someone speaking on the other side of the door. She held her breath and the door finally opened. The young doctor and the nurse who had brought them her cup of tea came in. She shut the door behind her.

"Mrs Burgess?"

"Yes?"

He motioned her to sit down. The four of them sat down facing each other. The doctor looked directly at Sarah and smiled sympathetically. "Mrs Burgess. I will be very frank with you. Your son is very sick. He has pneumonia and he can't clear his chest."

"Will he recover?" Sarah's voice was sharp and incisive as she interrupted the doctor.

He paused.

"I thought not."

"I'm very sorry Mrs Burgess. We will drain his chest and keep him sedated."

"How long?"

"24 hours. Maybe twice that. Not long."

"Thank you."

"I'm sorry."

"It's not a surprise."

Again she smiled.

The nurse said "You can be with him now."

"What's your name?"

"Nurse Jones."

Realising she could see that on her badge she added softly, "Laura".

"Thank you Laura."

Sarah and June nodded at the doctor and went back to Karl.

Sarah stifled a gasp as she saw him. He was grey and did not respond when they entered.

"He needs turning regularly. He can't turn himself."

"We know."

"I'm sorry. I'm not trying to tell you how to do your job. It's just..." There was a pause. "He's my son and..." Her eyes flooded, she choked on the words and then stifled it. "I just want the best, that's all."

"I understand."

Sarah looked at her and Laura felt her desperation. "We'll look after him and you can be here whenever you want to be." Sarah sat at one side of his bed, June at the other. She held his hand.

"I love you so much."

June bowed her head. Sarah had to be strong for her son and she had to be strong for her daughter and she did not want her to see her tears.

"It's alright mum. You can cry if you want to."

June nodded.

"If you need me."

"Yes. Thank you," and Laura quietly left.

They sat there for hours, through the darkness of the night and the slow blossoming of the new day. The only noise was the ticking of the clock mingled with the slow and feeble beeping of the heart monitor.

Next morning Mel and James came with their grandad. The nurses busily found chairs for all of them. They sat there sometimes silent, sometimes talking about little things, unconsciously getting ready to face what lay before them. They became used to Karl's silence that marked his absence from them. Together, they waited. By Wednesday morning they were all in a routine of shifts, taking time to eat and sleep, doing all the everyday things that people have to do. The situation became normal or as normal as it could be. Questions like "Any change?" replaced the look of fear and silence as people entered the room.

Sarah had not left the room, except to go the toilet. Her mum brought her wash bag and a change of clothes and the staff gave her meals. For the rest of the time she sat there, watching and waiting, sometimes sleeping.

On Wednesday Chris suddenly appeared. "I've just found out," he blurted out as he sat down beside her. He told Sarah how her neighbours had told him. In all the rush and confusion, no one had thought to contact him.

"How is he?"

Sarah snorted, "Not good."

"What has the doctor said?"

"There's not long."

142

Chris sank into himself and looked at Karl. He could see how weak he was. He was thinner than he had been on Saturday, noticeably so, and he was shocked at the sudden change. He stood up and leant over him.

"Karl. Hiya mate. It's Chris. We start the World Cup on Monday. You've got to get better quick. We don't want those tickets to go to waste do we?"

"He can't hear you."

Chris was surprised at her sharpness towards him, but he understood. He sat down beside and took her hand in his.

"How are you?"

"Oh I'm bloody fine I am. It's great isn't it?"

"I meant. Well you know."

She withdrew her hand from his and they sat there separately, watching in silence. Chris felt her indifference to him. It was more than just sadness. They were not together at this difficult time.

She was withdrawn and he a bystander. She did not need him there. After an hour of silence, punctuated by her grunts in response to his comments, her father came in. Chris got up.

"I'd better be off. I'll come in the morning?"

"Aye lad. It'll be good to see you. Karl would love to see you."

Sarah sucked in a huge intake of breath.

"He's not going to see anybody dad!"

"Aye, well you know."

The two men nodded to each other understandingly.

"Bye Sarah."

Sarah bade him farewell, but did not look at him.

Chris left. As he closed the door and turned to walk down the corridor June stood in front of him.

"She doesn't mean it lad. This is too much. She's not talking properly to any of us."

"Aye. I know, but I don't know what to do. I want to help."

"There's nowt anyone can do. This has to take its horrible course and it cares for no one. You have helped. You've made her and Karl so happy these past few months. You've been so important. She just needs to do this herself."

"Aye, well, tell her to call me when she's ready. Tell her I'll be there whenever..." His voice almost failed him.

"It's not easy for you either. I can see that. Take care lad. It'll be over soon enough."

They embraced. She patted him on the back in motherly fashion before parting. Chris walked up the corridor towards the car park and left. Meanwhile, June prepared to enter the room and help her daughter deal with the last minutes of her son's life.

Both of them sat there for the entire afternoon. At five Sarah's dad brought James and Mel and together they sat with the motionless figure in the bed.

The room was still. Outside, the heat of the day was beginning to subside and cars were starting to stream past as people returned to their homes. It was just another day, the same old routine with the same petty incidents that seem so important at the time.

Inside the room, things were far from routine. An expectant silence crept round its cream walls, as Karl's breathing became shallower and quieter. Once or twice it seemed as if his breathing had stopped, only for the oxygen mask to cloud up and then clear as his exhausted body summoned its last ounce of strength once more and then, once more. The slow pulsing of the heart monitor teased the small gathering.

Every half hour a nurse would come in and do a routine check, noting the readings on the monitor. Speaking softly she would apologise for her interruption and smile in that compassionate way that nurses do around death.

On the wall a clock ticked. Sarah sat holding Karl's hand as she had so often done in the middle of the night. She watched the movement of the hand as it counted the hours, the minutes to her son's end. She wondered if this was a clock that Karl would have liked, but decided that it wouldn't be one of his first choices. It was too functional for that. It had a white face with simple numbers round its rim and a red finger that counted the seconds.

Her son was lying in a hospital bed. For some 12 years her life had consisted of work without ceasing, on-and-on, like the ticking of a clock, tick bloody tock, on and on, towards this final awful moment and she noticed that the colour of the seconds finger was red.

She sighed and turned towards her son. She was so, so tired. She watched him breathe. She listened to him and she stroked his forehead with the back of the hand and then with her palm.

"I love you" she whispered.

Then from the bed he called "Mum"

"Yes?"

"Mum"

"Yes. I'm here my love".

"Mum".

Each time he called her his voice was weaker. Realising that he was having difficulty hearing her she moved closer to him. Her face was against his.

She put her lips to his ear.

"I'm here Karl. It's your mum"

She stroked his forehead again, first with the back of her hand and then with her palm as she always did and he knew it was her.

"Mum"

144

"Yes?"

"Will you turn out my light?"

"Of course I will, as soon as I get home."

Then the heart monitor signalled an alarm. Nurses walked in aware that no resuscitation was required and switched off the sound. The ward sister turned to Sarah and said "Mrs Burgess, I'm so sorry."

Sarah interrupted her.

"I know. I know he's dead. You don't have to announce it. Do you think I don't know what death is? I've been living with it for years. I know."

The nurses stood there blinking. June stood up. "We'll be alright."

"Of course. We're here."

"Yes, thank you," and with that they left.

Sarah stood up, rejecting her mother's attempted embrace. Her lip quivered like an upset child and it sent a shock wave through her whole body as she shook from head to toe.

"Mam."

Sarah put her hand out to Mel.

"I'm all right. We're all right," she gasped.

"It's all right."

Grandad sat holding James.

"I'm all right. I just didn't want that noise."

Sarah climbed onto the bed and lay beside her son. She took hold of his head and held it to her breast. She let out a groan from the depths of her being. A primeval force tore itself out of her body. It was a mother's cry for all mothers in all places throughout all history who have lost those to whom they have given birth.

She who had been so strong for so long was lost. She was inconsolable and there was nothing, nothing anyone could do. Sarah sobbed for two hours, but Karl never felt the heaving of her chest.

The red finger, in the clock on the wall, carried on its relentless journey unaware that time had stopped.

29. Farewell

The funeral was set for the following Tuesday. Sarah had wandered around in a trance assisted by the anti-depressants prescribed by Doctor Fitzpatrick to help her sleep. They had ensured a full night's sleep, now undisturbed by Karl's need to be turned, but they did not help her function in the daytime. Her mum and dad had made the arrangements for the funeral and also ensured that they were all fed despite Mel's protestations that she could cope.

In truth she was pleased with her grandmother's insistence. She needed some comfort and her mother was in no position to provide it. Sarah lost five pounds in weight in the time leading to the funeral.

She had not seen Chris at all. He had phoned three times, but she had not felt able to speak to him. He had asked Mel if he should come round, but she had advised him against it. Each time he had ended the conversation by telling her to tell her mother that he loved her and was thinking of her.

"She loves you too Chris, I think, but she's not in a state to deal with anything right now."

"No, I know." He paused uncertainly.

"I'll tell her you called."

That was the last time they spoke before he left to go Leeds to prepare for the World Cup that was to begin a week on Saturday.

The Great Britain team assembled in Leeds on Saturday to allow for a week's preparation in camp before the World Cup competition began on 15 October. To be a part of such a competition was something any professional sportsman would dream about. It was the pinnacle of a rugby league player's career and something Chris had believed he would never experience. Indeed, he wouldn't have done had fate not introduced him to Karl. Karl had shaken Chris out of his comfortable routine of training and playing and shown him that life was something you had to fight for. As a result he had removed some basic flaws in his game and now found himself in the national team.

Yet, as he sat alone in his hotel room unpacking his clothes, he felt empty. He busied himself by placing a stack of CDs, that would help him through the quiet periods of the next three weeks, onto a shelf, yet there was no enthusiasm. He finished unpacking and sat on his bed, his hands clasped together with his elbows resting on his thighs.

He had lost Karl and had had no contact with Sarah. He so wanted to speak to her, to comfort her. He would be attending the funeral. Sarah's mother had insisted that he come, but he felt awkward, uncertain if Sarah would want him there. He rubbed his face. Not to go would be foolish. He knew Karl would want him to be there. His family had become Chris's main preoccupation outside rugby and that was now broken. So he sat there in a deep melancholy his head bowed.

Suddenly there was a knock on the door that made Chris jump. He leapt up to open it. There stood his team mate Sean Wood. Chris's mood lifted immediately. Sean had that effect on people. He was probably the smallest man in the party and therefore one of the toughest. He had to be to survive on the pitch, but off it he was a character full of fun. Standing at around five foot six inches tall, red haired and freckle faced he had a boyish charm about him.

They were good friends. Wood walked into the room assuming an invitation to enter would be automatic. "Hiya!. Settled in then. God, you've got enough CDs."

"Yeah."

"Are you all right?" Wood sensed that Chris wasn't his usual self.

"Yeah. I'm just tired that's all."

He noticed a picture of Karl on Chris's bedside cabinet.

"Oh, I see you got a picture of that lad, you know, the cripple."

Chris continued to unpack and did not look at his friend who was a nice bloke, but not the brightest of people.

"He's not a cripple, he's disabled."

"Oh, right."

It was obvious to Chris that Sean did not understand the difference or probably even recognise that there was a difference.

"How is he?"

"He died."

It was the first time that Chris had actually said those words. They shook him and left him as open mouthed as his friend.

A moment passed. Chris almost laughed at Sean's facial expression and then felt sorry for him.

"When?"

"Wednesday."

"I'm so sorry. I took the wife and kids to Tenerife for a week. I didn't know. I hadn't heard."

"It's okay. Hey, it's not like it was unexpected or anything."

"No, but all the same. It must be hard for you. How's his mum?"

"I don't know. I haven't spoken to her."

He stared into the distance. "Or rather, she hasn't spoken to me."

"It must be so hard. Do you want to be here?"

"No. I want to be with her, but I can't do anything so I dunno. I might as well be here."

"I only met him once, but he seemed a nice lad."

"He was. Which reminds me, the funeral is on Tuesday. I need to ask David for special leave and I'm not looking forward to that.

"I'll come with you and see him."

Chris smiled.

"No, I meant I'm not looking forward to the funeral."

"Oh. I'll come with you to that if you like."

Chris stood for a moment holding the door to the wardrobe in one hand and a pair of jeans in the other. He didn't think Sarah would mind. Sean had been to Karl's party and had been well received. He desperately wanted to go to the funeral, but was wary of meeting Sarah. He felt that he should be by her side, yet she had not responded to his phone calls and had been in bed on the two occasions he had called. He didn't know what to do next. He could do with some company, protection perhaps, solace possibly.

"Yes, actually, I would like that."

"Right then. We'll see the boss at the end of the briefing session this afternoon," and with that he left as quickly as he had entered.

Chris smiled to himself. That was Sean all over, quickness of thought and movement that made him a more than useful ally on the pitch. Chris hoped that his charm would be equally useful off it.

He had just sat back down on his bed when there was another knock on the door. Chris sprang up, thinking Sean must have remembered something to tell him. He threw the door open. To his surprise, standing there was not Sean, but Lewis Jenkins.

He smiled. "Hi. Can I come in?"

Chris allowed him in uncertainly. He didn't feel like doing a follow up on the – admittedly kind – article he had done before.

"Have you seen this?" It was a copy of the *Gazette*. Chris looked at him, perplexed. "It's on page 42."

Chris turned and saw a headline which said, "Anderton set to sign for Wigan." His jaw dropped.

"There's no truth in it then?"

"Absolutely none. I've talked to no one."

"That doesn't mean your club hasn't."

"They can't do a deal without me."

"True, but they can engineer things to suit them. Word is that your chairman wants to capitalise on your growing reputation and do a deal while you're still hot property before people remember your age."

"Thanks."

"Well, it's a fact. Nobody's getting any younger as they say. Steer will see it simply as good business."

Chris sat on the bed in disbelief. Not only was he no longer interested in going to Wigan, but he didn't want any distractions in the run up to the World Cup. He wanted to focus on that and that alone. Then another thought occurred to him. He didn't want Sarah to think he was clearing off out of her life. This could have terrible repercussions. He crumpled the pages together.

"I can help you."

Chris looked at him, unsure if he could trust the journalist. Jenkins sat down on the only easy chair in the room. "I know about Karl and can I say I'm truly sorry. I know it was inevitable but, well, he was a great kid." He paused. "We could do both ourselves a favour."

"What do you mean?"

"There are going to be lots of reporters flying about trying to find a story. You're a prime target because of your association with the boy. It's a sad story and very newsworthy. They'll want to run stories monitoring your progress in the wake of Karl's death and so on. I could do a follow up story on you and Karl and we could aim it to scupper Steer's plans to transfer you. We could talk about your loyalty to your club and your young friend. It would be well received, a heartstring puller and allow you to counteract any attempt by the club to offload you to Wigan. What do you think?"

"I don't want Sarah to be involved or upset. She's got enough to contend with."

"Absolutely. No problem."

He had no choice. He wasn't able to talk to Sarah even if she knew about it. At the same time he wanted it to be seen that he was not going anywhere. Together they sat down and drew up the outline of a story that portrayed Chris, how he had been motivated by Karl and his loss would spur him on. It also talked about his sense of loyalty to club and friends and denied that there was any truth in the rumoured transfer to Wigan.

After Jenkins had left, Chris felt more settled. The story in the *Gazette* had bothered him. He didn't want any hassle. He wanted a clear mind, but there was more to it than that. Karl's death had not simply upset him; it had thrown his entire life into turmoil. He was no longer certain what or who he was or what course he wanted his future to take.

All that would have to wait now. He had done all he could to defend himself and to let Sarah know that he was there for her if she wanted him. Now he had a funeral to attend.

At 2.15pm precisely Chris, accompanied by Sean and Ian Duffy, Castleton's first team coach, turned right and entered the housing estate. Chris searched for somewhere to park.

As he got out of the car, the bungalows stood before him. He found himself noticing the presence of ramps, handrails and dipped kerbs. What the hell was going on in his head? He was here to say goodbye to a friend. It was a funeral for God's sake, but recently he'd thought about disability issues more and more recently. Like most people, until he met Karl he had given the issue of disability little thought. Now it was becoming a preoccupation. He had become increasingly aware that he was feeling a need to do something, something for others.

Although he hadn't consciously intended it, Karl had shown him that throughout his career he had been focused on himself, his achievements and his progress. The world of the entertainer or sportsman was such a selfish one, all about that all-consuming word, "Me". Chris was aware that he was undergoing a change in his outlook on life, but he wasn't, as yet, certain where it was taking him. All these thoughts raced through his head as he found a parking space.

The house was not difficult to find. The small car park was already full. A row of cars stretched down the street, hemming the house in. Neighbours stood on front steps chatting and waiting.

Incongruously, in the middle of this scene, life was continuing for others. Workmen, who were relaying paths around the estate, had deposited a mound of gravel in one of the parking bays. The pile was about four feet wide and seven feet long by two feet high. It looked like the topping of a freshly completed grave. For a brief moment Chris wondered whether he had been late for the funeral and had missed Karl's burial in such a convenient place, near his home. He smiled at the pile and then apologised to it for his sick humour. He knew Karl would have laughed as well. He'd probably arranged it as a joke. Then Chris stopped smiling. He took his keys and got out of the car.

A breeze wafted over them. Its cold touch reminding them that autumn was driving summer away. Lace curtains trembled in windows. There was a noticeable air of expectancy in the close. He could feel it. Karl would not leave unnoticed. People half smiled at them, pleased to see them, but aware that this was not a time for smiles. Some nodded and the men returned the gesture. One little boy, unaware of the gravity of the situation shouted out Sean's name. Sean smiled, waved and carried on walking. They were used to community involvement, but this was not their normal type of activity. Being a star on public view and being quiet did not sit comfortably.

A group of old women were gathered at the far corner. Some stood, arms crossed while others rested on walking sticks. One frail looking individual sat on a chair by her front step. Each new visitor produced a greeting of faint whispers as they tried to work out who each one was. Just as he was wondering whether any of these old ladies would have any inkling of who he and his companions were, one shouted "Hi Chris. Bad day eh?"

"Aye".

"He would be pleased to see you, wouldn't he?" She turned to the others who nodded in agreement.

"Oh yes, he loved his rugby," said another. Everyone nodded again.

"Aye, he did."

"He was a good lad. Always a good lad," continued the old lady.

"Yes he was." Chris paused momentarily and smiled.

"It's not fair is it?"

150

Chris looked at her. The group fell silent, expectant. What was he supposed to say? Was he expected to make things right? He settled for "No it's not. He was a good lad," and then after a moment's thought added, "a great lad."

Then a tear welled up in her eye. Chris gave her hand a squeeze, but he was no saviour. He wasn't going to make things better. He had to move on. "See you later."

The three men turned towards the front door and walked up the path in silence, taking care not to walk on the grass. It was time to do things properly.

Sean coughed nervously and Duffy fidgeted with the knot of his black tie. Used to wearing tee shirts and tracksuits, he had not worn a suit since the death of his father two years earlier.

As Chris went to press the bell, the door opened. James invited them in. Dressed in a black suit and tie that sat badly with his youth he turned to let his mother know that they had arrived. Sarah already knew. She was standing, talking to two other women at the other side of the small front lounge. He looked at her and she smiled. He was surprised how attractive she looked. He had never seen her with make up on. Make up that masked her complete exhaustion.

"I'm so glad you could come. Thank you."

"I had to come, believe me."

He took hold of her hand and she let it stay limply in his before letting it slip out.

"Can I introduce ...?"

"I know who you are."

She smiled at Sean and Ian and thanked them for coming, offered them a drink, and turned once more to Chris. "You were his hero."

Chris said nothing. Instinctively he took her hand once more and they stood there silent and motionless. He felt so sorry for her and yet she did not ask for sorrow. He had expected to see her vulnerable and weak, but instead she was calm and self-possessed. Was this a show or was she truly in command? Had she faced everything there was to face? Could nothing else damage her now? She seemed to glow in the midst of the black clothes. As the two of them stood there smiling into each other's eyes someone said "They're here".

Her hand shot from his and he saw her chest heave as her expression changed. Yes, she was strong, but it didn't mean that she was going to face the day easily. Everyone stood up together. As people moved to leave she stopped in the doorway and faced them.

"All through his life Karl never buckled once. We aren't going to falter now. We shall remember him and be thankful for him. We can cry at home."

It was a battle cry. People stood, looked at each other and nodded. This would be a celebration. They coughed, cleared their throats and filed slowly out.

The hearse stood there, its finely tuned engine running so perfectly that it was almost silent. The close was now filled with neighbours. Car doors opened and then clunked shut. Engines turned over and then revved quietly and respectfully into life.

Sarah and her children entered the limousine, the door held open by her father. When they were settled the driver of the hearse gently accelerated; it glided out of the close and moved effortlessly away with a procession of cars following behind. Neighbours dissolved back into their homes. Just one, the old woman, remained, staring after the cortege until well after it had disappeared. "Goodbye" she said quietly and then she, too, went inside. The close was silent, the car park empty, except for the pile of gravel.

The cortege arrived at the church some 15 minutes later. Although they only lived a stone's throw away it had taken so long because Karl had requested that his funeral should pass by the rugby ground. As it did so the hearse slowed to a walking pace. Sarah looked at the wall of the south stand where he had sat so many times and smiled for him and herself as she thought of all the happy times they had spent there. They passed in a moment and moved onward to the church of St Stephen in North Lane. It was a very imposing sandstone building despite the fact that it was quite small.

The hearse parked outside the gate. Reverend Stephen Foster stood waiting in his gowns accompanied by a throng of people. It had been a long time since the vicar had seen so many people at a funeral. He wondered whether there existed a mathematical formula that could calculate the relationship between the age of the deceased and the number of people attending the funeral. Older people had fewer friends because many of them had already departed. Younger people had friends, family and workmates. Karl seemed to be known by everyone. Reverend Foster had expected a crowd, but this was impressive to say the least. He greeted and blessed the coffin as the attendants took it from the hearse. They wheeled it through the gate and paused while the vicar talked kindly to Sarah and her children.

Foster had known the family for several years and although they hadn't attended church regularly they had kept in contact. He was also a member of the choir with Karl's grandad and had always kept an eye on Karl. Sarah had visited the church on occasions. He had the impression that she tried hard to hide her pain from her family and had been largely successfully. He had been concerned that she seemed unable or unwilling to share her fears with anyone else and had advised her to do so on several occasions. He realised, however, that she was trying to remain strong for all her children and that not speaking about her troubles was probably a coping mechanism. He had thought on more than one occasion that if she ever did show a chink in her armour, a dam would burst. He had therefore decided that he should simply be there for her whenever she needed to talk.

The conversations had often been strange given the circumstances. She did not talk about her feelings. She would come and talk about how the children were doing at school, shopping, decorating, anything but her troubles. It was as if they both knew she was in trouble, but rather than talk about it, she simply needed a place to sit and chat and so that was what they did. He hoped that he and his church had been able to act as a port in a storm for a ship that was sailing in treacherous, unchartered waters.

So, now as he welcomed her and her children to his church he had a mixture of feelings. He wanted to embrace and protect her, but she showed no need for protection. He wanted to console her, but she showed no need for consolation. He wanted to remove her pain, but she showed none.

As he shook her hand and held it, he studied her closely. Perhaps he was the only person who really knew her true state of mind. He knew her strength, but he was concerned. He did not believe that anyone was able to deal with something like this completely alone.

Having completed the greetings, he turned and led the procession containing Karl's family, friends and staff from school and college, members of his grandfather's choir, friends and neighbours, into his church.

Reverend Foster stood at the front. He saw that the church was completely full. When everyone was settled he began. "Dearly beloved, I would like, first of all on behalf of the Burgess family, to thank everyone for coming. We are gathered here today to remember and celebrate the life of Karl James Burgess. His mum has asked that we emphasise the word 'celebrate'. Karl would have hated to see anyone crying. He would have probably told people where to go in that quiet, charming way of his." The congregation smiled at this and it seemed to remove some of the tension in the gathering.

"Karl first came to my attention when he was 10 years old. He and the family had already come to terms with the implications of his terrible illness. I don't want to sound stupid or corny, but in many ways Karl was a lucky boy. I have never seen a group of people so bound together by a deep sense of love as Karl's family and without love we are nothing. With love we are everything. It is the meaning of life and Karl gave it and received it in abundance."

He had been holding onto his lectern, using it almost as a prop to guide him through. Funerals of children were always the most harrowing, but somehow he gained in strength and picked up on this

153

theme, moved away from his support and script and began to speak more freely.

He spoke of courage and fortitude, of humour and character and dignity. "Dignity." He punched the word out. "Dignity. He taught me the true meaning of the word. He was 17, still a boy, but in his death he taught me, all of us, how to live and that is a great gift."

He referred to a recent advertising campaign that had shown the disabled sign with the word changed to "Enabled". He railed against the notion that disabled people took from others.

"Of course they do but, most importantly, they give to others. They show us a way forward and that life is to be enjoyed and not wasted in self-pity."

He spoke of Karl's father, Dave, of Dave's kindness and his pride in his children and the love of his wife. At this point Sarah almost broke her command to others. She bowed her head and inhaled deeply as she struggled to breathe. Without faltering in his speech he moved forward and to his right, hand outstretched. He took her hand and continued.

They then sang a hymn and while the congregation sang he spoke gently to her. When she nodded to him that she was okay, he returned to the front and raised the volume of the entire gathering single-handedly. When the hymn was finished, Foster addressed the congregation once more.

"As you know Karl was an unusual lad and this is an unusual service. He had many interests. One was his love of rugby league. He had an encyclopaedic knowledge. Try saying that when you're drunk."
Again he made the congregation smile. He knew that the family did not want it to be a solemn occasion and was good at doing 'happy' funerals.

"I am pleased to see some players from Castleton have come. Karl would have liked that. He would have told you off for losing your last match of the season. Then he would have told you why you lost."
Again, everyone smiled.

"Another interest he had was the choir. He went every Wednesday with his grandad and I have a message for Grandad John. Karl told me a week before he died how much he enjoyed that time with you. He said that although it wasn't cool for someone of his age to like something like that he enjoyed most of the songs even though they were sung by old men."

There were smiles once more. "Don't the young have a great way of complimenting you? Anyway some members of the choir are here to sing one of his favourites. If you listen to the words ladies and gentlemen, you'll see why."

With that some 20 men from the congregation filed forward, dressed in evening suits, white shirts and bow ties. They assembled in front of the choir and sang a gentle song called *Tomorrow is another day*, about life in a hospice and how to deal with your troubles and pain. Its main theme was that there was always tomorrow.

"Here you'll find a haven, a shoulder to lean on.

Lay down your burden.

Tomorrow is another day.

Tomorrow is another day."

Throughout the song any close observer would have noticed that John struggled to sing the song. His body began to shake uncontrollably. Unnoticed by the rest, two members of the choir, standing either side of him, put their arms around him and held him while they finished the song. It was grandad's tribute to his grandson.

As he listened to the song something as equally profound was happening to Chris. A thought had occurred to him. If this thought had appeared six months earlier or even two months earlier he would have laughed at its absurdity. Now it didn't seem absurd at all. It made perfect sense. He could see a picture of his future beginning to develop. The vicar was right. Karl had not just received from others. He had contributed. He had contributed much more than he would ever know.

Chris was still deep in his thoughts when he realised that the attendants were moving the coffin and that the church ceremony was over. He caught a brief glimpse of Sarah as she passed, flanked by her two children. With arms wrapped round each other they half walked, half stumbled, behind the coffin.

Leaving the church the coffin was taken along the continuation of the narrow path that they had used to enter the church. Looming in front of them some 70 metres away was a pile of freshly dug earth placed next to a new hole that was partially concealed from view by a headstone in an earlier row. It was the longest 70 metres of Sarah's life. A large part of her life, their lives, was coming to an end.

She had held his hand in the night, talked to him for hours in the gentle lamplight and sat listening to the ticking of his clocks when he had fallen asleep and she was too tired to move. She had watched the lines on his face; his young face, too young for lines, get deeper and darker as his body tissue faded from his bones.

He had a beautiful face, too beautiful for this and she was proud to have known him and, despite the effort, she was pleased, no grateful, to have been his mother. People remarked on her forbearance and strength, but she had learned it all from him. She was proud to be his mother and she wasn't going to send him from this earth with anything less than the dignity he had displayed in life but as she stood there, the rock of the family, no one could detect that the strength was slipping from her. She was fighting to keep control of herself for him, but she was beginning to lose it.

She took a deep breath, several deep breaths and steadied herself. She looked at Melanie and James, "All right?" They nodded. They knew what their mother's question meant for they had talked about it and prepared for it. They stopped at the graveside. Sarah took their hands and squeezed them tightly. She smiled at them both and stood perfectly straight.

"We're all right."

In the October chill the sun was already falling. A flaming red sun sent splashes of pink dashing in and out of nervous white clouds as if trying to grasp them before they fled across the sky towards the dark. The wind, for the breeze had now become a wind, blew Sarah's hair in strands across her face and she tried to brush them away, but each time she did the wind gained revenge. At the far end of the graveyard a line of tall poplars held their near vertical branches upwards as if making an appeal to the Almighty. Their branches waved imploringly, as if trying to beg the clouds to stay a little longer, but on they sped regardless.

Further on a lonely willow tree seemed to bend over towards them offering its sympathy. The vicar finished his sermon, the time for humour had passed. Sarah stood motionless. As they lowered the coffin she didn't cry. She smiled and blew a kiss and said "Thank you". Friends and well wishers in turn came up to throw a handful of earth onto the coffin. Sarah shook hands or accepted a kiss. As everyone departed to the reception, she stayed there. As she saw Chris she smiled thinly, told her children to return to the car and that she would be along shortly. They stood there facing each other. He took her hand and she did not resist.

"I won't be coming to the reception," he said.

"Right" she said without asking why. Perhaps explanations were not necessary. People had to do what they had to and each would deal with this in their own way. Again they stood there holding hands.

Quietly he said "I'll see you. Whenever you need me."

"Yes. See you," and as he turned she said, "Thank you," and then she paused, "for everything."

Unable to speak he simply nodded and walked away. All the time he walked across the graveyard he could feel her watching him and all the time she stood straight and alone and still she didn't cry.

She watched him pass through the cemetery gate, and turn left towards the church before disappearing behind the hedge of Hawthorn bushes.

Suddenly she felt the bitter wind biting into her and she shivered. She looked at her son's coffin. Picking up some reddish brown earth she tossed it downwards. It thudded on the box and made a louder

156

sound than she had anticipated. It made her jump and then she laughed at her stupidity. Then she stopped. This was no time to laugh. She sighed, raised her face to the heavens and slowly a tear began to trickle down her face.

It was 20 minutes before they found her. At first the children sat waiting in the car. They saw Chris coming out of the church grounds. He stopped and talked to them for a few minutes. He told them to be strong for their mother and they nodded in agreement. He told them that he cared about them and that if they wanted to talk to ring him at any time. Melanie leant forward.

"She does love you."

"Yes I know." He raised his head above the doorframe for a moment, hoping that they would not see the twist of torment that swept across his face. He leant into the car. "Take care."

Then he was gone.

The brother and sister waited for their mum and then it began to dawn on them that she was taking a long time. James got out first and ran down the path towards the gates of the cemetery. He stood there panting as Melanie arrived at his side. At first they thought it was a black bag or something. Then they realised that their mother was lying in a crumpled heap at the foot of her son's grave. They shouted out and ran towards her. At the same time two workmen were arriving to replace the soil in the grave. They arrived at Sarah's side at exactly the same time as her children.

One of the men took off his coat and wrapped it round her. Sarah groaned that she was okay. "Well, we'll just make sure," said the man without his coat.

"No really. Please, I don't want a fuss."

They helped her to her feet.

"Are you sure?"

"Yes. I'm fine. Thank you. I felt a little dizzy that's all."

The man took his coat and the two children escorted their mother towards the car in the same manner that they had entered.

"What's happened?"

June immediately saw that Sarah was very frail as her grandchildren helped her into the reception room. She sank into a chair.

"I'm alright."

"You are not alright. You look terrible."

"Thanks a bunch."

"Can I have a glass of water please?"

June looked at her husband who brought back a glass of water and a whisky. Sarah shuddered as she drank the whisky.

"You need to see a doctor."

"I'm fine, honest."

"It wouldn't do any harm would it?"

It was the kindly, but authoritative, voice of Stephen Foster who had watched her entrance with alarm. Sarah was too tired to resist the extra weight of opinion and she succumbed to their wishes

30. The run

Chris woke as he always did at 6.30am. He was due back in Leeds at 2pm, but he had a regular training regime that he adhered to religiously. His first task was an early morning run which he liked to do before the rush hour.

Every other morning he would get up, put on his tracksuit and running shoes and run. Leaving his house he would smile at the milkman before turning right up the steep rise which, after half a mile led to the entrance of Taylor Park. He loved the park. He had played there almost every day of his childhood. Summer cricket would be followed by winter rugby with the occasional game of football.

Into the park he would go across the grass and through the bushes leading to the main path which he avoided as much as possible. He hated concrete and liked the natural feel of grass under his feet. Sometimes when he wanted some quiet he would sit and stare across the lake in the middle of the park at some distant bird climbing steadily over the hill. It was serene.

After running anti-clockwise round two thirds of its circumference he would attack the hill that rose from the far side of the lake reaching the top in a target of one minute before descending westward to the far exit. This track was hazardous as it was a minefield of slippery rocks ready to break an ankle of the unwary, but Chris knew it well. On the right the high stone wall of a barn gave way to a field full of cows. On the left a small embankment provided large boulders for passers-by to sit and ponder.

Here, suddenly, Chris threw his heaving body across the biggest. Lying on his back and gasping for air he suddenly realised where he was. He didn't remember getting dressed, or leaving the house. He couldn't remember the park. Were the flowers in bloom? Had he seen the milkman? He must have done the hill under his target time. Certainly it felt like he had as his chest struggled to get back to a normal rhythm but he had no recollection of what he had done since waking. Suddenly he sat upright as the realisation hit him.

Karl was dead.

This took his breath away more than the run. He collapsed back onto the rock before sitting up again. He sat there, staring, open-mouthed, before any clear thought entered his head.

Karl was dead.

A feeling of panic came over him. Of course knew he was dead. He had been at the funeral for Christ's sake. He'd driven home, had tea, cried, slept, gone for a run and yet, only now did he realise, did he realise that that young boy, that complete innocent, that fighter would fight no...

159

His thoughts stopped and he burst into tears. He sat there, elbows on knees, head bowed and chest heaving. Tears streamed down his face as he shifted from side-to-side trying to control his emotions. He was supposed to be a tough guy. What if someone saw him? His fingers snapped at each other. His hand ran through his hair. He could not stay still. Finally his body and mind succumbed to his grief and he cried inconsolably.

He was a six foot three, 17 stone rugby league forward. He was one of the toughest and strongest in the world, renowned for his ability to overcome others, but he wept for that little boy and his power, famed throughout his sport, could not protect him.

Chris had no idea how long he had sat there in a trance. His crying had been replaced by a stillness in his body. Then he sensed something. He lifted his head and peering through his parting fingers, he was shocked to see a cow standing only four feet from him. It stared silently at him. He had not been aware of its approach. He was touched by its calmness. Its silence seemed to embody the peace he was seeking.

From the rear of the cow a voice shouted an instruction, "Get along there. Go on!"

The cow moved forward without protest, eyeing Chris cautiously as it drifted almost gracefully and diagonally past him before trotting onwards down the path from where Chris had just come. His eyes followed the cow. It was as if something meaningful had passed between them as if, ludicrously, the cow was telling him that things were going to work out.

As Chris watched his new friend move away he became aware of the presence of other cows. Turning to his left he saw that a whole herd had advanced warily onto him. At least 20 cows had come close to him without him even realising it. For a minute he thought that he was going to be trampled, but at a further command of "Gowon" they shuffled past, followed by the voice.

The voice was possessed by a small thin man. "Mornin'" he grinned, revealing a mouth with only one tooth remaining in its lower jaw. The effect of this was such that his jaw seemed to jut out further than normal and his tooth resembled a tiny rhinoceros's horn.

"Don't see many people up here at this time. Come to think of it we don't see many people up here at all," the tooth smiled again.

Chris smiled back. "I come up here," he said. "But normally I've gone by now."

"I thought I hadn't seen you." There was a pause. "You're the rugby player aren't you? 'Chris'."

"Yes."

The tooth smiled and raised his head upwards in pride as if he'd just won *Mastermind*. "Ah hah! I knew. Yes, you can't fool me."

160

"I wasn't trying to."

Oblivious to Chris's reply, he carried on. "Oh yes, I've been watching Castleton for, oh, must be over 40 years. I remember the first game I went to in 1958," he drawled. "We beat Barrow by some ridiculous score. The weather was foul. It chucked it down. I got absolutely soaking wet."

As he spoke, he arched his back and wagged his finger as if he were delivering a lecture. As he continued Chris became aware that the cows had carried on past the farm gate on the left. Indeed the leading cow seemed to be heading down the path towards the park entrance.

"Er, excuse me"

"Aye?"

"The cows don't appear to be following orders."

The tooth did not take in Chris's observation. He held the lapel of his overalls like some learned lawyer in the middle of a speech.

"Yes, man and boy, man and boy," continued the tooth, oblivious of his cows making a break for freedom.

Chris held his hand up like a small boy at school nervously trying to attract his teacher's attention. "The cows."

"You know, me and the cows are like clockwork. Here we go every day exactly at this time, without fail, ready for milking. The cows can find their own way really. They don't need me. I could turn them out of the field and down here they'd walk, no hurry, and into the yard they'd go. If the milking shed door is open they walk in. They're cleverer than people think."

"The cows!"

"What?"

"The cows." Chris pointed.

The tooth's jaw dropped. "Fuck me! Come on!"

Without thinking Chris followed obediently.

"But I don't know what to do!"

"Never mind. Stay calm!" he shouted, panicking. "Do as I say."

Unfortunately the act of running had the effect of driving the cows on and the entire herd began to turn into the park at greater speed.

"Stay calm! Stay calm!" the tooth said, his arms and legs gyrating outwards in all directions.

"Stand there" he said, pointing to the far side of the entrance, "and make certain they don't turn right when they come out of the park!"

This was ridiculous. Chris was used to tackling 17 stone forwards but not one ton cows. How heavy were cows anyway? Too heavy! That was certain. He could hear the tooth, now some 50 yards into the park shouting and wheezing his commands.

"Gowon. Gowon!" was followed by silence. Suddenly a bovine head peeked round the sandstone pillar of the entrance. It looked like his friend from earlier, but he wasn't sure.   It looked as if it was weighing up its options.

"Gowon." He shouted, copying the tooth, whereupon it turned back into the park blocking the path of the others as they came out.

"What the f...." came from the other side of the hedge and Chris found himself tucked up in laughter as the poor, confused cow turned once more on the command of the tooth. This time Chris waited, letting the lead cow come out of the park before waving his hands. Fortunately the cow turned left and the others followed. As the last one left the park it became obvious that the lead cow was heading back past the entrance to the sheds and up to the field.

"Jumping Jesus. You stupid, bloody animal". Every word was punched out individually to stress that he meant what he said and once more the tooth had to overtake the group and turn them back. The cows mooed in disapproval.

"Ah shut the fuck up!" shouted the breathless tooth.

This time the cows obediently turned into the yard. They stood there mooing in protest, swishing their tails from side-to-side and turning their heads to look disapprovingly at the stranger who had spoiled their fun. Chris felt guilty. As they finished shutting the gates the tooth turned to him and grinned.

"Just like a game of rugby! Trying to make a set of overgrown blockheads do as they're told!"

"Thanks."

"No offence."

"None taken". Chris smiled. There was an awkward silence as the older man struggled to get his breath back.

"It's a grand morning," he said.

"Aye, for chasing cows! We should do this as part of the training." They smiled.

Then Chris began to laugh and the tooth joined in nodding and winking at the rugby player come herdsman, but they weren't laughing at the same thing. Chris was laughing at the ridiculousness of the situation. Here he was supposedly in mourning and yet having the time of his life. In the middle of tragedy stood comedy. Then he stopped laughing and he smiled politely and the tooth grinned back, oblivious to his companion's torment.

The cows stood waiting impatiently to enter the milking sheds. When he had got his breath back the tooth walked across and pushed the doors back. The cows entered and moved towards individual bays.

Eventually when all the cows were being milked the tooth emerged from the last bay, wiping his hands. He was grinning again. Chris had stayed in this foreign environment and not thought to move on.

"Syd Arkwright." He extended his arm and they shook hands. Chris was struck by the strength of his grip. He wasn't a big man, but years of hard work had kept him lean and tight. "I've been farming here for 40 years and never had that happen." Then, there was another pause as the tooth wiped his hands again.

"You're playing well just recently."

"Oh, am I?" said Chris, surprised at the sudden change in the conversation. "Thanks."

He felt awkward talking about himself. This time wasn't about him.

"Beginning of the season I thought you were finished, past your best, but now out of your skin, you are."

"Yeah..."

"What caused it?"

"How do you mean?"

"What caused the change?"

"I don't know," he said, hesitatingly. He knew that Karl had caused the change, but he didn't want to talk about it, not now. It wasn't the right time and yet he found himself doing so.

"It was nothing conscious. It was something that just grew on me."

The tooth nodded.

"It was a lad, a disabled lad."

"Oh I read about him, shame. Real shame that was. Yes I read about him."

Chris continued as if the tooth had not spoken. "It was supposed to have been the other way round. I was supposed to have helped him. I was supposed to help raise money to help him. Jenkins was right."

He turned to the tooth who nodded in agreement despite the fact that he didn't know what Chris was on about.

"Jenkins was right. He saw it first. The kid helped me. He knew more than I did," and then he smiled. He smiled because now he knew what was going to happen. He'd felt it in the church or rather he'd sensed it, but it wasn't clear. The revelation was almost biblical.

"I was unsure as to whether I would be able to continue."

"Are you okay?" said Arkwright.

Chris turned to him. "Okay? I've never felt better!"

"Thank you," he grasped Arkwright's hand and shook it vigorously, almost shaking the little man's entire body.

"Thank you."

"For what?"

"For asking the right question!"

"But I only asked what had produced the change?"

"I didn't know where this was all leading to, but I do now!" Chris shouted as he stepped out of the sheds, trotted carefully over the cobblestones, passed through the gate, making sure it was locked. He looked at Arkwright and shouted across the yard: "I have a job to do! Thanks."

"But!"

163

"See you!"

"You never gave me an answer"

"I will. After the last match! Bye!"

With that he turned and left Arkwright perplexed, but pleased that he'd been able to help. "All the best for Saturday! You're going to need it." he shouted as he watched him disappear into the distance. "I'll be there!" and he turned to tend to his cows whispered quietly to himself.

"Glad I helped."

Chris had left his house in a daze, functioning on automatic pilot, but now he felt really good. He added another two miles to his normal routine to make up for the rest he'd had at the farm and flew round with a stupid grin on his face.

By now the rush hour had begun. Some children shouted from a passing bus and he waved back. It was good to be alive.

Normally he jogged the last half mile as part of his cool down, but he had not realised he was home until he stood on his front step gasping for air. His hand shook as he inserted the key into the lock. He wasn't certain whether this was as a result of his exertions or his suddenly discovered happiness. He took a bottle of milk from the fridge, kicked off his trainers and sat on an easy chair still chasing his breath. He looked at a picture of Karl on his coffee table and gave him a toast.

"Thanks mate."

He drank the last of the milk and wiped the remains from his lips.

"I won't let you down."

31. Wilson

The tournament completed its qualifying rounds in three weeks. Great Britain won all three games against Samoa, Fiji and a weak Russian team. Chris played in the first two games and scored in the first before being rested for the third. At least he hoped he was being rested and not dropped. The coach had said that he was giving others an opportunity to press their claims for a place in the team.

After each game Chris would return to his room and smile at Karl's picture. Later on, after the couple of drinks that they were allowed as a post match celebration, he would imagine the picture in his room while sitting in the bar and would quietly say a toast to it. Sometimes he would talk to the picture as part of his preparation. He knew that others might consider it foolish, but it suited him.

The team to play in the Saturday's semi-final was to be announced on Thursday. While selections in the earlier rounds indicated how the team was shaping up in the coach's mind, the team selected for the semi-final was particularly important. It showed the likely selection for the Final, always assuming that they managed to beat the formidable New Zealand team. Team selection was the sole responsibility of the coach, George Wilson, an Australian.

He was now 49 years old and had been in charge of the British team for five years. He had taken the job knowing that it would be a huge task to beat the Australians. Britain had not won a test series against them for 30 years.

His strategy of turning to youth had gone well and he had introduced numerous young players into the full British team. However youthful enthusiasm was never going to be enough. He needed something else, something indefinable. That something had fallen into his lap and was unexpected. It was Chris Anderton.

Chris had qualities no other player had. He was enthusiastic and experienced. He had watched Chris on many occasions and regarded him as a good player nearing the end of a satisfactory career. He had seen him as capable of excellence, but not quite having the consistency or self-belief to deliver at the very highest level.

His performances this season, however, had been a revelation. He was regularly winning the man-of-the-match awards. He had been selected for Yorkshire in the Lancashire versus Yorkshire series of matches that served as trials for the World Cup squad. His performances in those games had ensured him a place in the squad. It was as if his career had been reborn. He was enthusiastic, dynamic and experienced. He could not be ignored.

His selection had another unintended, but useful consequence. It had produced a lot of interest from the media. Anderton was in demand. Writers wanted to know what was behind his change of fortune. They wanted to know what effect his selection would have on the youth policy. It was a sort of story the media likes and rugby league was getting headlines in the sports pages that it rarely got. They could not ignore a good human interest story and Chris's rise from being close to retirement to international level was just the kind of story they liked. That it involved a disabled kid facing death was even better for the media.

On Wednesday evening Wilson had asked Chris to come to his room for a chat. Chris was a little concerned. He had felt that his two games had gone well, but missing a match always made a player feel vulnerable, despite reassurances from the coach.

He climbed the stairs to the next floor with some trepidation. Was he going to be let down softly, told before the announcement that he wasn't playing? He felt like a naughty child arriving at the headmaster's office as he knocked on the door.

Wilson opened the door, smiled kindly and ushered Chris in. Already waiting was John Clarke, the team manager, who was responsible for all the administration that kept this group of young men operating. Both men smiled and shook Chris's hand before inviting him to sit with them around a coffee table.

On the table lay some newspapers.

"Have you seen these?"

Chris said that he hadn't. He hadn't looked at a single paper for the last fortnight. "I don't like the rubbish they write, but I am aware that they've been saying things about me."

Clarke, a young man in his late 30s, studied him and smiled. "If we'd have known that we might not have bothered having this meeting. Have other players not said anything to you?"

"No." Chris was perplexed.

Wilson leant forward and opened the sports pages of three papers. They all had a picture of him and Karl and ran stories about Chris being in a state of mourning for his lost friend. They questioned his ability to perform adequately. What was also disturbing was that each story ended almost identically with the same opinion expressed that a loss of form could affect his impending transfer to Wigan.

Chris sat bolt upright as he read the articles. He was visibly upset. These stories were more than just stories about a transfer. False rumours were to be expected sometimes, but this was personal. Not only did he not like the invasion of his grieving for Karl and the discussion of its possible effects on his form, but he didn't want Sarah to think that he might be leaving, nor did he want her to think that he had been involved in using Karl's death to produce heart tugging stories to promote the competition. He was confused and alarmed.

166

"I'm sorry Chris, but we had to speak to you. Even if you haven't read them, the lads have. We thought it would be wise to see how you were."

"I'm fine. I'm bloody annoyed, but I'm fine."

He was not fine though. He was trying to think what to do. He didn't care about the stories for himself. It wouldn't affect him or his rugby but he was bothered about Sarah. These thoughts were pulsing through his head when he heard Clarke's voice again.

"Well I'm glad that's cleared up then. We just didn't want you to be affected by these stories." He smiled and then said "It's a bad business with this young lad."

"Yes."

"If you don't feel up to it."

A sense of panic snaked round his insides pursued by anger that Clarke was more concerned about the possible effect that Karl's death might have on his playing prospects than he was about Karl himself. Finally confusion slithered in. There was no need for guilt. His had been a perfectly reasonable response and he felt the need to defend himself.

"I'm fine, honestly. I understand the situation."

Wilson stared at him closely. "I don't want to sound callous. I really don't, but we have to make certain, for your sake as well as the team's that you are up to this."

Chris stared back at his coach and found himself speaking in a quiet and purposeful manner that was alien to him. "I have been honoured to have met a very fine young man. I promised him that I would bring him back a medal and I'm going to do my best to make sure that happens."

The three men sat across the table staring intently at one another.

"Good."

"Can I go now?"

"Of course."

Wilson saw him out and watched him as he descended the stairs. He was concerned about Chris's effect on team morale. He had not told Chris that he would be playing in the semi-final yet, but he saw him as the key player in his plans. He would be the experienced core of a young team

He had to ensure that the death of that kid, tragic as it was, did not harm his capabilities. In fact he had to find a way to ensure that the boy's death enhanced them. He would use any means open to him to win, even emotional stories in newspapers if he had to.

Back in his room, Chris was agitated. He was under the impression that Lewis Jenkins was going to write a friendly story, but he'd seen nothing. He wondered what was happening. He sat on his bed, his

167

arms folded tightly around his chest, trying to think. He picked up the phone and dialled. A woman's voice answered but it was not Sarah's.

"Is that June?"

"Yes?"

"It's Chris."

"Oh, hello love. How are you?

"I'm fine thanks."

"You've done really well. I've been watching. We've all been watching. Are you going to be in the final?"

"I don't know yet. We've got to beat New Zealand in the semis first. They announce the team tomorrow."

"I'm sure you will. You've played so well. Our Karl's coaching really paid off then. He must have known a thing or two."

"Oh, he certainly knew his rugby."

"I say a little prayer for you every night. Karl's watching over you. I'm sure."

Chris was uncertain how to reply. He laughed softly in agreement. He didn't share June's conviction, but he was aware that he had felt something, a spirit maybe or just a memory surrounding and guiding his every move. For a moment they were silent, both knowing what the next question would be.

"How is she?"

"She's doing okay. It's not been easy."

"No."

"It must be hard watching your daughter go through this."

"It's hard for all of us."

The word us gave a strange sense of inclusion that he hadn't felt before and he realised how much he wanted to be involved. There was another silence and again they both knew what question was next.

"Is she there?"

"No, love." She heard Chris's sigh.

"She's asleep. The drugs knock her out."

"Drugs?"

"Painkillers and anti-depressants."

"Painkillers?"

He didn't question the anti-depressants. That was to be expected.

"She had a fall after the funeral." She heard a gasp. "She's just bruised that's all. She's over it now."

"Will she see me if I come back?"

June tried to stay calm. "Listen. It's not the best time. She doesn't want anyone to see her just yet. She's not at her best. Anyway, you've got a job to do haven't you?"

"Yes but..."

"Well then."

Chris had to accept defeat. He knew he wouldn't be able to see her, but at least it didn't appear like she'd read the papers.

"Anyway you need to win that medal. You've no idea how much that means to us."

Chris limply put the receiver down. He wanted to believe what June had said, but somehow in his lonely hotel room it all seemed to be becoming a little pointless. His mind kept shifting between feelings that it was the most important thing he'd ever done and feelings that promises to the dead might just be words spoken to someone who was no longer listening. He was beginning to feel desperate.

He was not alone. June walked down the hallway to her daughter's bedroom to check on Sarah. She was fast asleep as she had described, but June was worried. Sarah had bruised her wrist when she had fallen in the graveyard, but her main concern was that she had hardly eaten for two weeks and had lost weight. It was as if Karl's death had caused a dam to burst and the flood waters had stripped her of the will to live. She who had been so strong for so long was in a state of collapse.

32. The last dream

She had not eaten for three days. Food is unnecessary when the body is too numb to feel hunger. People spoke, but their words had no meaning. They talked in slow motion, their voices deepened and distorted.

Their faces blurred in a fog. She listened, but their words washed over her and floated away. People came into the room and went out.

She was not certain what room she was in, but presumed it was her bedroom, although she recognised few of the contents.

She can't remember who had been in.

She needed company, but she wanted to be alone.

Nothing mattered.

Nothing mattered.

There were no words to describe what was happening to her.

There were no words. She was in agony and yet felt no pain.

She grieved for her lost son and for herself, for her life too, had ended. It had lost its purpose. It existed around him.

She fed him.

She washed him.

She dressed him.

She toiletted him.

She turned him in the darkest hours of the darkest nights.

She comforted him.

She loved him.

She lost him.

She was lost. She was empty.

Now she could sit and rest all day if she wanted to, but she could not. She had lost the habit of resting. It was alien to her. Instead she fretted and polished. She polished items she had already polished twice before. She could not be at ease.

She was confused.

She was both grief-stricken and thankful.

Grief-stricken because she had lost her child and no mother should endure that, but thankful that it was all over and he was at rest.

Finally, one more emotion dug its way into her. She felt guilty.

Guilty that she might one day enjoy herself.

Guilty that she can now take a bath for as long as she likes. She can light candles, burn incense sticks and sink into a warm luxurious bubble bath and lie there and let the world...

Guilty.

She was grief-stricken, exhausted and... guilty.

Sarah's dream had returned. She was surrounded by darkness. Her emotions had been ripped to shreds by a court filled with her loved ones, but still she functioned, managing to keep her life and the lives of others together. She was the fulcrum, the pivot around which other people lives moved. She had held it all intact, until now.

She lay slumped on the floor with her knees bent underneath her. Her back rested painfully and awkwardly against the cliff face and her head is tilted towards her right side. She did not move.

She could not move.

Her matted hair fell over her face and half obscured the dry, cracked lips desperate for water and the bloodshot eyes devoid of rest.

She heard a noise. It was the familiar noise of his wheelchair, a mixture of a whirring electric motor and tyre rubber gripping on a slippery floor. She heard the click as he moved the drive lever forwards. He emerged out of the darkness and stopped in front of her. He said nothing.

She sat upright. Her lips hurt as she spoke.

"Karl?"

He did not speak.

"Karl. It's me. It's mum."

Silence.

"I'm sorry. I'm so sorry. I know it's my fault. I gave birth to you. I should have known. I'm so sorry. Please help me. Please!" She was sat up on her knees with her hands clasped together, praying, begging. "We had no idea. We'd never heard of it. We didn't know that it could happen to us, to you."

She paused, but he stared through her as if he was looking into her soul. She was totally exposed. "I don't know what to do. Should I? What would you think? I never wanted him to replace you."

She was babbling, ranting, not appearing to make sense. They stayed there striking a pose, locked together in silence and time. Then suddenly his right hand moved. It put the chair into reverse and he moved back into the darkness.

"Karl! Karl, please help me. Don't leave me. Please Karl help me!"

She reached out only to find that her arms are held by chains she had not noticed before. She wrestled with them, pushing them away, pulling them right and left, but still they held her. Then she saw that the chains were changing form. They are someone's arms holding her. She could hear her mother's voice calling. She was shouting to her from some distance, calling her name. Sarah panicked and screamed. Her body arched violently, before collapsing back on to the bed only to arch once more.

"Mother!"

"Mother! Help me!"

Sarah knew that this was her chance to escape from the ledge. After being imprisoned for so long she could be free.

"I'm here love. I'm here. Shhh..."

Suddenly her mother was close. She could see her. Mum was holding her. Sarah awoke, smiled at her mother and laughed weakly before collapsing into the gentle restful sleep of an exhausted prisoner who had been rescued and was now free.

But Sarah was not free, not yet and nor could she ever imagine herself being. For the time being all that registered with her was that, somehow, for some reason she had been rescued and just like a hostage, rescued by some special forces, she is grateful, but shocked. Why should she be rescued now? There was no apparent reason. Maybe there was a purpose, but it was one that was beyond her tired eyes. Like a freed hostage she rests, troubled by her peace of mind

She woke up and found herself alone. She had no sense of time or day. She did not know how long she had been in the bed. She moved about the house with no particular purpose, wandering through its silence. She walked past his bedroom and paused, slowly opening the door and looking in. The room was dark because the curtains were drawn. His bedside clock ticked its familiar tick. Immediately she recognised its sound and a whole lifetime swept over her. His wheelchair stood empty, silent, as if it was watching her, having assumed some of the human qualities of its former occupant. She expected it to say something, but it didn't. It seemed to mock her. Is she awake or is this a return to the dream? Has she ever escaped it? Is it all a dream? Her reality has become dream like.

She touched it. Pressing its drive control it moved as if it had come alive and she jumped, but did not speak. She did not turn the light on, nor did she open the curtains. She moved in the darkness. There was no need for light. She knew every inch of this room. She stood at the computer desk, looking at the blank screen. Her fingers slid along the keyboard. The room needs dusting, but she left it as it was. This room was central to his existence and it will not be disturbed. She did not know why she was there. Perhaps she was looking for a sign. Perhaps she would receive a message on his computer. She told herself not to be stupid.

Her annoyance with herself broke the trance. She looked about her in surprise for she didn't remember walking into the room and the absence of mind disturbed her. Quickly she left. She closed the door as if resealing a tomb. She stood there holding on to the handle, breathing heavily and allowed her fingers to fall away, one by one.

This is the moment that Sarah realised, consciously, for the first time, that he was dead. He wasn't there anymore. Once that realisation sunk in something happened that is impossible to explain.

She smiles.

She thinks only of him.

His pain is over.

Sarah leant her head against the door, took in a deep breath and exhaled slowly. As she did so she became aware of the muffled sound of the television coming from Melanie's room. She knocked and entered. Lying on the bed together are her two children. They had been watching television together and had fallen asleep. She stood there, smiling at them, listening to them breathe. After a minute or two, she turned to press the off switch. As the programme disappeared from the screen Mel woke up and sat up with a start, almost bouncing James off the bed.

"What!?" he cried.

Seeing the look on his sister's face he turned and together they both stared in surprise at their mother.

"You're awake" they both said in unison.

"How long have I been asleep?"

"Nearly a week."

"It doesn't feel like I've been asleep."

"Grandma said it was the tablets."

"Where's grandma?"

"I'm here" said her mother as she walked in with a cup of tea.

"How did you know I was awake?"

"I heard you. Then I saw you go into his room."

There was a silence, broken when James got up and wrapped his arms round his mother's waist, almost knocking the cup of tea out of her hand. Melanie half smiled, slowly got off the bed and put her arms around her in a tender embrace. Grandma took the tea from her daughter and placed it on a coaster on the chest of drawers.

"I'm hungry."

"Good."

June had never enjoyed preparing a meal so much in all her life. She was so pleased. Sarah was hungry.

33. The Final

Sarah took two more days to recover from her drug-enforced slumber, but she did not have a visit from her dream.

On Friday she walked into the kitchen. Her mother handed her yet another cup of tea. It slid comfortably and luxuriously down the back of her throat. As she finished she put the cup down on the table and noticed before her an envelope.

"Did you just put that there?"

"It's on Saturday."

"What is?"

Sarah knew what her mother was referring to, but she didn't feel quite ready to deal with it.

"You know what they are."

Suddenly Sarah became very serious. She took the envelope in her hand. She could see the words "The Rugby Football League," on the heading of the covering letter. She examined the tickets carefully, as if they were some prized jewels.

"Do you think I should go?"

"What do you think?"

"I don't want to, but I feel I ought to, for him."

"Do you think it would matter if you didn't? You've been through so much. I'm sure he'd understand."

"I promised him I'd take him."

Sarah said nothing as she considered her options. She stared at the tickets. "Do you think Chris would want me to be there?"

"It's what you want to do."

"Do you think he cares still?"

"I know he's rung you several times and each time we've made excuses for you."

"Has he? Why didn't you tell me?"

"You said that you didn't want to speak to him."

Sarah sat up with a start. "I don't remember that."

"You were so tired and so out of it." She paused hoping her daughter would say the words she wanted to hear, but Sarah said nothing.

"What are you going to do?"

"I'm not sure."

June sat down gently, drawing the chair up to her daughter's side.

"Love, sometimes you get an opportunity in life and when you do you should take it, even if the timing isn't right."

She took her daughter's hands in hers. "I don't know what's right, but I do know you deserve to be happy. You deserve it and that man is the best thing that's happened to you since, well, since."

She had nearly said 'since Dave' but had managed to stop herself. She realised that it was not sensible to even hint at comparisons, that she should talk of only Chris, emphasising the future. She did not want to give Sarah any chance to let the past prey on her mind again.

"You were going to say 'since Dave'."

Sarah saw her mother's discomfort and smiled, but said nothing. She was thinking.

June stayed focused on her daughter's eyes and for a fleeting moment she thought she saw something that suggested a change in outlook, but it passed. Perhaps she had simply hoped for it.

"Anyway, think about it. That's all I've got to say love."

June went home and the children went to bed. Sarah sat for hours alone in the darkening room, in silence, thinking.

She looked in the mirror of her dressing table and was shocked. She held the greasy strands of her hair, twirled them between her fingers and then rejected them in disgust. She noticed a photograph of happy times. She saw a boy with his mother, brother and sister on a beach, smiling, and she recognised the woman. It is herself and she was surprised how happy they appear.

She had forgotten.

She showered and came out of the bathroom wiping her hair with the towel. She was dressed in her tattered pink dressing gown that she had never thought to replace. She had never noticed its poor condition, until now. She entered her room and sat at her dressing table again. The bedside lamp shone a soft light onto the mirror. Taking her hairbrush she slowly, weakly pulled the brush through her wet hair. This soothed her. She stared at the image in the mirror. She recognised it, but was surprised to notice that she's older than she remembered. Her trials and tribulations had taken their toll. This woman looked exhausted and drawn. There was a weariness that sleep cannot relieve and yet she was still here, battered – but not defeated, a warrior who has faced everything and survived.

She saw the tired lines, premature ageing and she put down her brush. She looked at her reflection who had been through so much with her and half smiled.

Together, in mutual support, she sat there looking at the mirror. Then, silently Sarah admitted something she had never said before. She didn't want to be brave anymore. She was sick of being brave. She had never wanted to be brave at all, but had never had a choice.

All she ever wanted was to lie in bed and be comforted, to be reassured that everything was going to be okay. She returned the brush to the box she kept it in, the box set that he bought her one Christmas. She placed it carefully beside the comb and closed the lid, ensuring that the clasp was closed firmly. She rested her hand softly on it and smiled gently, weakly. She looked once more at the mirror.

They smiled at each other knowingly. Taking a long breath, as if in preparation for effort, she stood up, still looking at the mirror. She pulled the belt around her dressing gown a little tighter, examined the frayed fabric thoughtfully before turning and leaving the reflection behind her for the final time. She said goodbye to this tired soul. They would not meet again. She had made a decision.

Sarah turned out the light and quickly slid under the duvet. It was time to sleep and this time to rest.

Saturday arrived; World Cup Final day. Sarah went about her business as normal. She had told her mum that she would be fine and wouldn't need any help. June did not argue and was only too pleased to take the chance to go shopping with her husband and James. They had not been out together for ages. Everyone had marvelled about Sarah's strength, but she would be the first to acknowledge her mother's contribution and support. Sarah watched her parents drive off and heaved a sigh of relief. She had already packed off Melanie to her boyfriend's house with a suspiciously hearty breakfast.

"Okay, what do you want?"

"What do you mean?"

"This meal. What are you after?"

"Nothing, honest. Can't a mum treat her daughter now and again? I realise that I've been neglecting you and I just thought, well, I just thought I'd do it. That's all"

"I love you mum."

"I love you."

The conversation had turned serious in a way she had not predicted or wanted.

Within half an hour Melanie had gone, however, and Sarah relaxed. She was alone and could make preparations. In the morning she went shopping before calling into the hairdressers for her appointment. She couldn't remember the last time she'd been to the hairdressers without feeling that she had to get back home soon. She had all day, well nearly all day. She had other things to do.

She had lunch in a little café before returning home. As she slid into the bath she almost gasped in pleasure and relaxation. She had never felt so happy, relaxed and excited all at the same time. She took a deep breath and drifted off into a relaxing sleep in warm water laced with scented, soothing bath oils.

She woke with a start and splashed water over the side. Fearing that a long sleep might have wrecked her plans she hurriedly checked her watch. It was 2.15pm. She had only slept for 10 minutes, but she was refreshed and ready. She got out of the bath.

Sarah dressed herself in some practical warm trousers and sensible boots before sitting in front of the mirror to put her make up on.

She took out a red bag with "Castleton" written on it in white letters and pulled out a Great Britain rugby league shirt. The shirt was white with a large red and blue Vee on the front. On the left breast was the picture of a lion and an inscription that said "Great Britain RL World Cup 2009". She laid it out on the bed and stroked the creases out of it. For a moment she stood there, admiring the bright colours and smiled. She thought how nice it looked and how pleased Karl would have been.

She pulled the jersey over her head gently to avoid disturbing her hair and make-up and stood in front of the mirror admiring herself. She turned and looked over her shoulder to check the back that she had already checked in the shop. On her back was written the number 11 and above it the name "Anderton".

Sarah smiled gleefully. She was proud of him. There had been a slight concern over whether he was going to play. He'd taken a knock in the semi-final victory and had been substituted, but it had been announced that Chris would play in the final.

It was time to go. She removed the bag from the bed and tidied everything away. She went out to her car. She slid open the side door of the specially adapted vehicle which she would have to return the following Monday. Dropping down the ramps she returned to the house and brought out his wheelchair. She pushed it up the ramps, wincing as her bandaged wrist felt the strain and locked it onto the floor-mounted clamps behind the driver's seat.

It was 3pm. Kick off was at 6.15pm.

Sarah had told no one what she was doing because she had feared that well-meaning people would insist on being with her and she did not want that. She was doing this for Chris, for Karl and most importantly for herself. As she drove up the hill and out of the estate she had never felt so happy and full of purpose.

That morning the team had eaten a hearty breakfast. The atmosphere was subdued in the dining area. Chris was unsure as to whether this was a good thing or not. The team didn't want to be too noisy because that would suggest that the players were nervous too soon, but neither did he want the team to be down. "They're very quiet." He whispered to Wilson.

"Yes they are. Don't worry though. There's a long day ahead."

After breakfast they held a team meeting at 10am. Wilson spoke to the players briefly about the expectations of the day before dealing with practical matters. He had announced the team on Thursday so the players knew who had been selected, but Wilson always felt that a ceremony of presenting shirts to the players was important.

One by one, the players walked up for their shirts to applause from their fellow players and officials. Suddenly the tone, so quiet before had lifted noticeably. "Wilson knows what he's doing," Chris thought to himself. Their preparation had been meticulous.

At the end of the meeting Chris nipped to his room before anyone had noticed he had gone. He was supposed to return the shirt to the kitman for safekeeping, but that could wait for one moment. He stood at his door checking both ways as if he were about to commit a crime. He entered the room and closed the door quickly before taking the shirt out of the wrapper. He laid it out on the bed and stroked the creases out of it. For a moment he stood there admiring the bright colours and smiling. He thought about how nice it looked and how pleased Karl would have been.

He pulled the jersey over his head and stood in front of the mirror admiring himself. He turned and looked over his shoulder to check the back. On his back was written the number 11 and above it the name "Anderton".

Chris smiled gleefully. He had worked so hard for this and he wanted a few moments to enjoy it before he started to play the role of the seasoned professional. After enjoying a few minutes of child-like delight, he took it off and returned it to its wrapper. It was time to go. He removed the shirt from the bed and tidied everything away. He checked everything and left.

To keep players occupied and their nerves at bay, Wilson had arranged for the team to visit The George Hotel in Huddersfield. It was here that 22 northern rugby union clubs had met in 1895 to form the Northern Union, a breakaway from rugby union over the issues of 'broken time' payments for their working class players when they lost money missing work to play in and travel to matches, and their desire to play in competitive leagues and cups. This new organisation became the Rugby Football League in 1922 and became the modern game of rugby league. The hotel had a museum about the history of the sport. There were pictures of great British players from the past, such as Gus Risman, Jim Sullivan and Chris's particular hero, Alan Prescott.

In 1958 the British Lions had defeated the Australians in a three match series in Australia. Alan Prescott, the captain and prop forward, broke his arm in his first three minutes of the second match. At that time there were no substitutes allowed. Prescott played on despite the doctor insisting at half-time that he should come off. As a result of Prescott's heroics, Britain won and went on to retain the Ashes in the next match. Unable to play in the next match, he was carried shoulder high around the field, his arm in a sling when Britain had won.

Chris came away feeling proud of what he was involved in. He could see that pride in the rest of the team. "Wilson certainly does know what he's doing." Chris smiled as the team boarded the bus to return to the hotel for an afternoon nap. They had a light lunch and left for Manchester. It was 3.30pm. Kick off was at 6.15pm.

Players had been in camp together for six weeks. They were now to face the ultimate challenge of their careers. The team coach moved out of the hotel grounds unnoticed. The atmosphere was strange. Players were almost silent on the journey. That is normally a bad sign as nerves take over and stop players from preparing themselves properly. This silence, however, was purposeful. They were thinking. Over the last week their physical preparations had gone well, but the management team had been working on mental preparation for the Final as well. Every comment had been positive and assertive. Wilson had had players considering their reactions to different game situations. Always, the outcome was a victorious one. Seeds of doubt weren't allowed. Wilson had left the young men in his charge no doubt that he expected them to win and that they had the ability to do so. Chris was reminded of what Karl had said to him. "Every day I have to think positively or else I wouldn't get out of bed. If you only think you might win then when the going gets tough and things go wrong doubts creep in and you are defeated. You have to believe you will win right up until the moment that you cannot." He should have been a coach. Chris smiled.

The coach slipped off the M60 at the sign that directed players and spectators to the stadium. Within a minute the sky suddenly darkened and the lights on the coach's dashboard seemed to glow brighter. No one had noticed the black clouds charging in from the west. The sky became as black as night and rain hurled itself onto the coach's roof.

Rain mixed with hailstones battered the ground and bounced two feet in the air before running in torrents towards already overpowered drains. Within minutes rivers formed in the gutters. Inside the coach the effect was mesmeric. It seemed like the coach was in a dark tunnel safe from the elements, but cut off from the rest of the world by a sheet of water and a wall of sound.

In this cocoon Chris's eyes closed and he drifted into a light sleep. He had always surprised others by his ability to sleep even in the most trying circumstances. Normally the rocking motion of the vehicle lulled him into child-like peace. Now his comfort and shelter was complete and he slept. Karl's face emerged in front of him He was smiling. This did not alarm Chris, nor did it disturb his sleep. He simply felt himself smiling back. He was content. In front of the biggest challenge ever to face him in his sporting career Chris Anderton was more content than he had ever been. The feeling that this was going to be his day washed over him. It just had to begin.

Suddenly the bus slowed to a crawl. Chris awoke and he could see dimly the flashing lights of the police motorcycle outriders. They were almost there. The rain had gone and suddenly slivers of pale blue could be seen attacking the blackness. The fans recognised the coach with the Great Britain team. They seemed determined to enjoy themselves no matter what the elements threw at them. Chris watched as the bus approached the final 200 yards to the stadium. The players could hear supporters shouting their encouragement and he could see the effect it was having on the players who waved and smiled as they passed by.

When Karl told him that he was going to die, Chris thought that he had put everything into perspective. He was just playing a game. When Sarah had corrected him and told him that it was important if Karl said it was, he had tried to believe her, but it was only now as he looked out onto the people going to the final that he fully understood. This was important. Karl wanted it. He wanted it and he hoped that Sarah wanted it to. He looked at the smiling, cheering faces. They wanted it.

He had a job to do. As they turned into the main entrance flags splashed against the darkness. A multitude of club shirts were on show as the coach came to a halt and the cheering became almost overpowering.

For a moment he thought he saw her in the middle of it all. He thought he had seen her pushing an empty wheelchair by herself, but the figure had disappeared as quickly as it had appeared. He shook himself in disbelief, dismissing it as wishful thinking mixed with his sleep-filled vision of Karl.

The engine died and immediately the party stirred into action. "This is it," shouted Sean Wood. All the party instinctively shouted back in kind as tension released itself. The manager smiled.

"Okay lads. Let's get off the bus first!"

He wanted the players wound up and ready, but at the right time. He didn't want too much emotion to drain the players nor did he wish to quash it. It needed to be just right. He smiled in a reassuringly, fatherly way before leading his team off the bus through the cheering fans and into the stadium.

Sarah was aware of the strange looks as she walked round the main entrance to the stadium. She passed the massive superstore, selling its football souvenirs and shirts. She marched resolutely on to the wheelchair entrance as indicated on her tickets. She was not deterred by the storm. She had done her best to shelter from the downpour. As her hair, so well styled those few hours before, disintegrated into a dripping mess she looked down at the puddles of water gathering on the leather seat before running off to the sides. The puddles emphasised the fact that there was no one in the seat and she felt silly and vulnerable. Then she remembered her purpose, dismissed her fears and marched onwards in the rain while others fled from it.

She handed her tickets in and the assistant took her and the chair up in the lift. As she exited to turn onto the specially designed platform he turned to her and said "I know who you are. I'm sorry."

Sarah looked at this earnest young man. "Don't be sorry. He's here with me. But thank you anyway."

The young man nodded and said nothing before re-entering the lift to collect his next set of customers. Sarah smiled kindly at him and watched the doors slowly close on him. She turned and pushed the chair into position and sat down next to it.

Tony Kettley, the kit manager and his assistant Sydney Smith opened the coach's storage compartments. They dragged out two hampers of clothing, medical equipment and drinks. Nothing had been left to chance. Finally everything; players, managers and equipment had forced themselves into the changing rooms in the bowels of the stadium. The door shut and suddenly there was quiet. The players sat down and began to prepare.

There is something interesting about any dressing room before a big match in any sport. Every type of character appears. There are the reserved ones who say nothing. There were old hands who had been here so many times before. They were simply busying themselves getting ready. Then there were the chatterers who babbled their way through their nerves.

Many players were very superstitious. One always put on his left sock before his right. A wrist bandage was put on his right wrist before tying his boots although his wrist wasn't injured. The reason for this was that he had once played an exceptional game when he had been injured and so the bandage had stayed. Many players believed that rituals such as these ensured a good game.

As players settled and completed their preparations, George Wilson who had been quietly going round each player distributing little bits of last-minute advice turned to address the whole squad. The men listened: "Right guys I'd just like a few words please. Now we have come a long way in a short time haven't we? We have done very well, far better than I had hoped could be possible. We know what we have to do in order to win today and that's what I am looking for. Simply do what you can control and don't worry about what you can't. The answer to victory lies in your heads and how you apply the things that you have been taught. I am not going to say any more, except..."

He paused. Wilson was always thoughtful and analytical. Some people mistook this for coldness, but those who knew him knew better. He had his feelings like anyone else. He simply didn't let them get in the way of his role as a teacher and organiser although this day was something different. It was a defining moment in his career and in the careers of the young men before him. It could also, possibly, be a defining moment for British rugby league.

He had thought about his next words very carefully and decided that perhaps sometimes, just sometimes, a little emotion might just go a long way. So what he said next was carefully prepared although the players saw it as something spontaneous. He paused, shuffling his feet from side-to-side.

"You know, I would like to say this. We have been working together for the last few years and in detail for the last six weeks. I know I'm Australian, but it has never occurred to me to think about anything else than the success of this British team."

He paused and everyone found themselves waiting for his next words as tension began to mount. "You are a fine body of young men. I really mean that." As he said it he held the thought as he looked round every player. "Whatever the result today, and you are good enough to win, I want you all to know that I am so proud to have been associated with you. You have strength, skill, courage and determination. I know that whatever the result, you won't let your country down." He paused again choosing his timing carefully. He held on to their expectant faces and said "I expect you to win."

Then he turned and walked to the door and opened it. Standing there he turned to them once more and said "Good luck. It's been a pleasure. Thank you."

With that he was gone, and the rest of the support team filed out. Just the 17 players remained. For a moment silence was all that could be heard as the effect of Wilson's simple words sunk in. He had managed somehow to deliver passion and emotion in a calm and analytical manner. The players sat there. They weren't going to let anyone down because he expected them not to and people rise to the expectations others have of them. These young men were sure of themselves. Nothing could stop them. Andrew Daniels, their captain, put his hand into his bag and pulled out a brown envelope. He took out 17 black armbands and passed them round. Each man put one on his right arm.

"Right," he said. "We know who these are for." Everyone in rugby league knew about Karl. This was the player's salute. "These armbands are my team talk. That's all I'm going to say." Still the silence remained until Wood, the team's natural talker, spoke.

"Right, all week they've been telling us that they are faster, stronger and better looking than us." There was silence. "So I propose just one thing. Let's go out and stuff 'em." Immediately there were smiles and laughter that broke the tension. Chris felt a sense of purpose within them. They were not going to be beaten. It was not exactly a strategy for winning a top-level international game, but they already knew what the strategy was. That had been gone over time after time in the week's preparations. Now the players knew that the result would be down to three simple questions:

How much?

How much did they want it?

How much were they prepared to give?

How much were they prepared to take?

In a moment the referee's whistle would blast down the corridor telling both sides that the time had come. Everyone fell silent with his innermost thoughts. The noise of the stadium tried to creep down the tunnel as the young men settled down before facing the heat of battle. Chris looked around him and was impressed by the way the team had come together. He closed his eyes for a moment and Karl's face forced itself into view. Surprised Chris opened his eyes before shutting them once more

He was still there and, try as he might, the image would not go away. He had not intended to see Karl. His appearance at this time had not been planned.

He decided that he would use his face as a motivator. Others had to find their own. While this was a team with a collective will, it was also a group of individuals fitting into that collective and they had to find their own means of inspiration. Karl was Chris's. It was the need to fulfil this boy's dreams that had got him into the team and it was that same need that would see him through the game. As the referee's whistle sounded to call the teams out into the players' tunnel he knew he was ready. He stood up. Seventeen young men put their arms round each other and stood in a circle.

"This is it boys." said Daniels. "You know what we have to do. Let's do it". Again the whistle sounded. There was a loud thumping knock on the door, as the man in charge of proceedings demanded their presence. They lined up behind their captain who opened the door to a wall of sound from the crowd. With scarcely a look at the green and gold shirts that were coming out of the door opposite, they moved in single file towards the tunnel entrance that led onto the pitch.

Every step produced an increase in volume until they stopped at the tunnel entrance waiting for the signal to enter the arena. Every player was trying to stay calm and focused while their hearts fluttered and danced and their stomachs churned. In a moment things would be better. They would be on the pitch. The formalities would be over and they would be able to run, to handle the ball, to settle the nerves before kick-off. But now they had to wait and everyone's, even the most seasoned of players, nerves jangled.

Then a section of the crowd, opposite to the tunnel, caught sight of the teams. They could see the captains twirling a ball in their hands.

The noise spread even louder as word of the teams' pending arrival spread round the ground. 60,000 voices began to shout "Britain, Britain, Britain." In reply 8,000 Australians mounted a heroic resistance. Many had travelled from London's sizeable Australian community. Others had travelled from Australia as part of a travelling army of 2,000 supporters.

Suddenly the signal was given and they were out into the bright floodlit arena. The noise of the fireworks and the crowd was deafening.

Chris surveyed the scene in front of him. He felt its power. He smelt its desire. Every sense was operating at full stretch. He stood there in the tunnel near the back of the team. This was the moment he and Karl had worked for. He had never felt so alive and he knew he was ready. It was time to move.

Walking out onto the pitch a great roar greeted him. It was both frightening and exhilarating at the same time. Chris found himself grinning whilst others grimaced and like Sarah he had never felt so happy and so full of purpose.

Led by their respective team managers the two columns moved slowly and with dignity to the centre of the pitch. As they did so hundreds of cameras flashed and died like shooting stars in the night sky. The teams meandered round to the centre. Both captains were introduced to the Prime Minister who in turn introduced their teams to him. After this was completed, an opera singer sang the national anthems and then the crowd roared once more as the teams broke away to opposite ends of the pitch. Players jogged and sprinted, feeling the turf beneath them. Now there was no turning back. Combat was about to begin. The captains shook hands and tossed a coin. Great Britain would kick off.

As the ball rose into the air from the centre spot 13 players in white dashed forwards. In any rugby league match, the first tackles can set the pattern for the whole game, Three British forwards arrived simultaneously as Andrew Bell, the Australian scrum-half caught the ball. All three tackled him, knocking him down with frightening force. Undaunted, the Australian captain rose to his feet and played the ball. As play moved leftwards he sank to his knees, looking towards the bench in expectation of treatment. Within seconds he was restored to good health. No quarter was going to be asked, or given. From a scrum, some 20 metres from their own line, Britain began to work the ball upfield. Unfortunately, John Briers dropped the ball in a tackle and Britain were forced to defend their line, putting them under immediate and unnecessary pressure.

Chris sprinted from his defensive position trying to ensure that he put maximum pressure on the Australian attack to stop their fluency of movement. Again Andrew Bell was the victim; Chris clattered into him, knocking him down with maximum force. Then the whistle blew. To his dismay Chris saw that he had been penalised for offside. Geoff Hamilton, the referee, called him to one side, explained that he wasn't going to allow any rough stuff and warned Chris that any further indiscretions by him would result in a 10 minute visit to the sin bin or worse, a sending off for the rest of the game.

He returned to his mark. He was fuming. Had he been over zealous in the tackle? He was sure he hadn't. He was hyped up, certainly, but he wasn't over the top. It was too important. This was the most important game of his life. Too important to make silly errors like that and yet he so wanted, needed to win to fulfil his promise. He wasn't going to get it wrong.

The whistle blew to restart the game. Immediately Bell darted towards him. It was the clever thing to do; attack a player who has just been punished for his defence. As the scrum-half rushed in Chris prepared for the collision only for the number seven to suddenly swerve to Chris's left. The defender responded immediately moving towards him, wrapping an arm around his waist, but the movement had drawn in another defender from the left. Jim Davidson was a huge man, over six feet tall, 17 stone and hard as nails. Both defenders were forced towards each other and with a sickening thud their heads collided, laying both men out in an instant. Freed from their grasp Bell shot forward at tremendous speed diving over the line before anyone else had a chance to recover. It was the worst of all starts. Great Britain were 6–0 down inside four minutes and had two key players lying semiconscious on the floor.

Chris hated smelling salts. They meant trouble. He detested the strong odour combined with an immediate feeling of nausea as he awoke from his enforced sleep. He was dimly aware of being lifted up and moved towards the dugout. What he was not aware of was that the collision was being replayed over and over again as the television commentators analysed the movement. The game had been stopped as medics from both sides rushed to help. Head injuries are serious at the best of times, but the television replays showed Davidson falling awkwardly. Everyone in the stadium could see fellow players grabbing hold of his prostrate body and turning him over into the recovery position to make sure that he didn't choke. The replays also showed blood spurt from Chris's forehead as he fell to the ground. Indira Higginbotham, the diminutive physiotherapist ran to him. One attendant sat him up while she held a swab to his head.

The crowd was silent. There is always something disturbing about 68,000 people who are not making a sound. It is frightening. Two stretchers were brought out. The medical team carefully lifted Davidson onto one with his legs strapped together, suggesting that he had broken a leg in his fall. The crowd politely and supportively clapped as he was borne towards an ambulance waiting outside. Two minutes later Chris was lifted groggily to his feet and, supported under each arm, wobbled towards the dugout. His face was smeared in blood and he was oblivious to the spectators' sympathetic applause.

As he sat down his head started to clear, he began to realise that this may be the end of the game for him and the end of his promise to Karl. This was not what was needed. He had to recover and get back onto the field, but every time he lifted his head he felt sick.

"Stay where you are!" said a voice. It was John Williams, the team doctor. The players respected him, so Chris didn't argue. He unceremoniously removed the swab from Chris's forehead. "That'll need stitching. Bring him to the medical room."

Chris was now able to walk with Indira's steadying hand assisting him. Williams already had his gloves on by the time Chris sat down.

"He doesn't mess about" Chris thought to himself and was pleased to realise that he was thinking. "Maybe I'm not out of this yet."

His thoughts were immediately terminated by the insertion of five stitches in his scalp with no local anaesthetic. It was the doctor's job to get players back out as quickly as possible. He had to supply the coach with fit players, although he always had the final say where a player's fitness to play was concerned.

"How do you feel?"

Chris was just about to lie that he was feeling much better when Wilson bounced in.

"How is he Doc? Can he continue?"

"Yes he'll be serviceable once I've put this padded bandage on. As for his brain, I'm not so sure."

Williams smiled to himself, but nobody copied him. He was well known for his calmness under pressure. Sometimes he irritated the more intense Wilson, but the coach knew that the doctor was good at his job.

"Take 10 minutes and then we'll see how you are." Anyway, now that we've lost Jim Davidson for the whole game, we'll need you to help the younger lads in the second half. So take your time." Chris nodded. He then turned to speak, but the man with the ruthless smile and red hair had gone, like a ghost, back to his seat in the stand. When he got back to his seat what he saw was not good. Britain had conceded another try and were now 10 points down. If ever a team needed inspiration, it was now.

By half-time Britain had exchanged penalties with the Australians and managed to steady the game down so that the half ended with them 12–2 down.

34. The final hooter

As the fans and television commentators pondered over the game's fluctuating fortunes in the first half, the British dressing room was a hive of intense and purposeful activity.

Some players sat drinking energy drinks. Another sat sucking on an ice cube in an attempt to reduce the swelling on his bottom lip and stop the bleeding. Chris's replacement, Stuart Farrar sat with a cold towel around his neck trying to cool down an overheating body. His throat burned with effort and he choked trying to force up phlegm and ease his chest. Chris was now clear-headed, if not exactly free of pain. In fact his whole head throbbed and his senses balked at every movement. He stared into space aware that the left side of his head was swollen beneath the bandage.

"How are you?" Wilson asked, smiling.

"Fine, boss. Fine"

"Are you sure? I mean absolutely sure? I mean, could you do 40 minutes?" The two men stared at one another. Two men preparing for battle, both aware of what was being asked.

Wilson looked into Chris's eyes. Chris looked back.

"Absolutely."

The coach touched Chris's shoulder like a kindly father. "Good. We're going to need you my friend." Wilson had a way of making people feel important without realising he'd done it.

Chris sat there proud of his coach's faith in him and the moment seemed to refocus him. In the struggle with his injury he had temporarily forgotten Karl. Now he remembered. He had a job to do.

Wilson was in the middle of this activity talking quietly to some individuals and remonstrating with others. Five minutes before the end of the break he told his charges to settle themselves down. He wanted to speak to them. An atmosphere of intense activity gave way to calm.

"Guys, we've done fantastically well." Chris was amazed and yet not surprised at these words. They were 10 points down to a team they were not expected to beat. He had received a nasty head wound and another player had been taken to hospital, yet here the coach was telling them how well they had done.

"We started off badly. We conceded an early try and suffered two injuries, but they haven't scored for 20 minutes. Guys we've stopped them." He paused to let these words sink in. He repeated them meaningfully. "We have stopped them. Now we have to put them in reverse. You know what you have to do."

Then he walked out and went back into the stands to watch. His job was done. It was up to them now.

As the players got up to return to the pitch Chris moved to a position near the door. Without saying anything he adjusted the black band on his arm as if it were part of his clothing. It had meaning, however. It was saying to his comrades that he was back with them and it was gentle reminder of Karl. It was telling them not to give in.

"You must believe you will win until it is clear you cannot." Karl's words were in his head. He hoped they were in everyone else's

Meanwhile, on the wheelchair platform on row 26, Sarah sat quietly by herself. She was worried about Chris. Sarah knew that injuries were part of the game. She had had plenty of experience looking after her brothers when they had been hurt. Chris had been hurt before, but head injuries were nasty and dangerous if not treated properly. He had not reappeared by half-time and her concern was growing. She had looked along the team bench and had scrutinised the television screen when it panned along the dugout, but there was no sign of him. She wondered whether he had been taken to hospital and was anxious not only that he might be badly injured, but that he would be devastated to have missed most of the game. Sarah touched the wheelchair as if to elicit some response, but none came. She thought about how Karl would have reassured her that it was all part and parcel of things and that he would recover. Suddenly as she rested her hand on the arm of the chair Sarah felt very lonely in the middle of all these people.

She wanted to leave but was compelled to stay.

She had to be there to keep her son's chair company and she had to make sure that Chris was okay. Under immense pressure and unable to move, Sarah stayed and hoped.

Suddenly, the players emerged from the tunnel, ready for the next 40 minutes, and a great roar enveloped her. It seemed to wake her and suddenly her panic attack ended. She rose and cheered as heartily as she had done when watching her brothers years ago. She was aware that Britain were behind and of course she was desperate to see them recover. Then to her immense relief she saw him walking behind the main party towards the team benches. Sarah stood watching as his breath evaporated into the damp night air. He seemed to be fine. Sarah sat down and clasped her hands to her mouth in restrained joy.

Chris was desperate to get back onto the pitch, but had not been called on after 10 minutes of the second half, despite his coach saying he needed him for the full 40. He was getting anxious and fidgety and no one had said anything to him. With only 20 minutes left Britain scored, reducing the deficit to only four points. Then Wood slotted over a penalty to reduce the deficit to just two points. Chris began to think he would not return because the team were fighting back without him. Perhaps the coach was protecting him. Perhaps it was all over. Then he heard the assistant coach's radio crackle in the dugout.

Alex Robinson, one of the assistant coaches, turned to Chris. "You're on. The boss said you had to go out and win it."

Ten seconds later Chris was on the pitch. As he strode on the whole stadium roared to greet him.

In the stands George Wilson watched without any obvious signs of emotion but Chris had been right. The boss knew what he was doing. He had turned a disaster into an opportunity. He was not keeping Chris back to protect him, but to unleash his pent up emotions. When Chris stepped across the touchline wearing that bandage on his head he looked heroic. It lifted the crowd, but more importantly it lifted the team. With 10 minutes left George Wilson had let one word creep into his thoughts. That word was "maybe".

Twenty feet away from him Sarah's ecstatic scream was lost among the other thousands of cheers that greeted the man she loved.

The floodlights seemed to glow even more brightly. The grass appeared greener and the white lines on the pitch stood out more clearly. As the colours intensified so did the tension in the crowd and among the players.

"Ref, ref how much time?" screamed Chris as he packed down for a scrum near the Great Britain line.

"Soon" blasted the ref. "Play"

The ball entered the scrum. Immediately Daniels, the British loose-forward picked it up at the back of the scrum and charged right as Wood, the scrum-half who normally took the ball swept left as a decoy. Australia's defence fell for it. Daniels drove forward at speed, making 30 metres before being felled. He quickly got to his feet to play-the-ball to a supporting player who resumed the drive before the defenders got back into position. Another 30 metres gained. Within two tackles Britain had entered their opponent's danger zone, 20 metres from the Australian line. They had done well, but it was now or never as time was running out. Two more attacks saw some resilient defence as the Brits were driven backwards. On the fifth tackle Britain's players exchanged glances. Everyone knew that this was it. This was their final chance. As Australians moved to make the sixth and final tackle, the British supporters despaired. It seemed that everything was lost as the vociferous Australian fans began to count down "7,6,5,4,3,2!". The noise reverberated round the ground and drowned the noise of the hooter that indicated that time was up.

They cheered their side's victory. They hugged, danced and clapped and were unaware of what was happening on the pitch.

One man, however, was aware. Lucas Roberts, the Australian coach saw that the British attackers were alive to their task. In rugby league the game ends after the hooter only when the ball goes out of play or a tackle is completed, but the ball was still in play. Australia had not completed that final tackle. Kelly screamed. Would his players be as sharp as their opponents and sharper than their own spectators who had only just begun to realise that the game was not yet won? Eight thousand Antipodean jaws stopped cheering and simultaneously dropped, to be joined by 60,000 more as the entire stadium woke up to the fact that Britain were still attacking. Quickly the defenders re-aligned. Three defenders hit Chris simultaneously, but somehow he managed to pass the ball rightwards. Wood kicked the ball 30 metres across field to right centre Malcolm Parry who stretched his huge frame to pluck the ball from 10 feet in the air. As he did so his opposite number crashed into him sending the ball luckily into Paul Wilkinson's hands.

Newspaper reports the next day would describe how in 12 seconds the ball was moved through seven pairs of hands and across the pitch twice. The effect was to produce holes in Australia's defence and as their now silent spectators watched in horror as the Great Britain left-winger raced clear. With only the full-back to beat he slipped a perfect pass to Chris who had got up off the floor to rejoin his comrades.

As if in a beautiful, silent dream, he glided gracefully in slow motion and yet still the defenders could not catch him. He dived over the line to touch down near the posts. He lay there on his back, gasping for breath. Later, he would explain it as being caused by a temporary lack of oxygen in the brain caused by his extreme exertion, but as he lay there, a face, large, pale and transparent, smiled down at him. It was the face of a young man, thin and weak projected into the sky. Despite the screams and cheers of 68,000 people shaking the stadium to its foundations, Chris saw and heard no one else except this face. It was smiling and thanking him. He lay there as if injured, but he was smiling, in a world of his own. It was a beautiful world of peace and quiet, of hero worship and gratitude. It was a gratitude that travelled both ways.

In that moment Lewis Jenkins's words rang true. Not only had the man helped the boy, but the boy had helped the man. Chris had achieved everything he wished for in rugby league and would cherish this moment all his life. A career that had been virtually over had now ended on the greatest note possible. In that time lying on the ground, with the sweat and condensation visibly rising from his exhausted body, Chris knew completeness. The boy had delivered this to him and his life would never be the same again.

He walked back to the centre spot as Wood slotted over the conversion of his try. Great Britain had won. Chris had won the man-of-the-match award in recognition of his resistance to injury and his determination. The try merely confirmed the correctness of the decision.

He waved to the crowd and then he noticed it, the empty chair and the reddish brown hair sat next to it. He raised his hand and then he cried. Everyone thought that they were tears of joy but they were not. They were tears for the empty chair. Tears for his lost friend, his unlikely mentor and they were tears for the woman sat next to the chair. He wondered if, hoped that she was all right, but he had no way of finding out.

She did not return his wave. Chris looked down at a small child who had run on to the pitch to be with her heroes. He said a few words to her and by the time he looked up again Sarah had gone. His emotional state had sunk from its highest level to its lowest in a moment. He scarcely felt the pats on the back and all through the presentation of medals his mind was elsewhere.

The photographs would show him smiling. They were proof of his presence, but a denial of his emotions. 68,000 people were saluting his deeds. Tomorrow's back pages would laud the heroics of a "Wounded Lion". He would be a local and national hero. Pictures of his scoring the winning touchdown would feature in the history of the game. No one could have achieved more and yet all he wanted was to be with her.

Despite the cheers and the frenzy of congratulations sounding from a multitude, he had never been so lonely and so empty. After the presentations and awards Chris left the field with the others, uncertain whether he would see Sarah again.

Sarah had left soon after the match had finished. She was ecstatic and had not realised that another 20 minutes of presentations would occur followed by television interviews and a lap of honour by the victorious Great Britain team.

In reality there was no point in her staying as she could not talk to Chris. It had not occurred to her that he could wave to her as so many other players were doing to their friends and family.

At the end as Chris scored she had jumped into the air and had suddenly felt sick and dizzy. She sat down to steady herself. Then she saw an image of her son in front of her. She thought she must have been hallucinating due to a lack of oxygen caused by her sudden physical exertion. The image seemed to be very real nevertheless and she didn't know whether to feel pleased or not. All kinds of emotions were swirling in her head from joy to a great sadness that Karl had not lived to see it. The image faded as quickly as it appeared and Sarah decided she had to leave.

She negotiated her way out of the stadium and through a small number of joyous fans who were also trying to avoid the inevitable traffic. Leaving proved to be a lot easier than arriving. Earlier she had felt nervous and tense. She had been nervous because she had never been to such an occasion by herself and was very aware that people would notice her pushing an empty wheelchair. She had also felt tense because she was also a rugby fan and had wanted her team to win. She had also been worried about Chris. She knew how important it was to him.

Now as she made her way to her car she felt vindicated. The cheers that still lingered with great force inside the stadium warmed and supported her. It had been almost perfect.

"No, not almost perfect, perfect."

She smiled to herself as she switched on the ignition and the engine fired into life. Within two hours she was home. Once she got away from the traffic around the stadium the motorway had been clear and her journey had been an easy one. She had enjoyed listening to the match reports as she drove home. She entered her front room to be greeted by her children and parents.

"Well it's obvious where you've been," said mum.

"Wasn't it marvellous? Did you see it?"

"Aye, we saw it. Chris did well."

"Oh yes!" Sarah was aware that she sounded like a schoolgirl. "I've never enjoyed anything so much since, since I can't remember."

"Good. I'm happy for you."

Sarah was aware of a tension in the room, but she ignored it. She knew they'd probably been worrying about her, but she did not feel guilty. She had done what she had to do and she had had to do it by herself. What she didn't know was that her mum had guessed where she had gone. It was not such a surprise. She had ordered everyone to make no complaint about their concern for her. All that was important was that her daughter had come back happier than she had been since any time she could remember.

After spending a pleasant night with her parents and children, Sarah went to bed, leaving the dishes until morning.

Chris entered the dressing room 30 minutes after the final hooter had sounded. He had been interviewed by three television channels and the lap of honour round the pitch in front of ecstatic fans had taken nearly 20 minutes. He had signed so many autographs and been kissed so many times that he'd lost count. It had all been wonderful and he had decided, very quickly to put Sarah to the back of his mind. This occasion had to be savoured. It was truly a once in a life time moment and he realised that it would have been a criminal waste to ignore it. He showered to a chorus of songs sung loudly and out of tune by young men who didn't care. They had prepared so well, kept their bodies in top condition and were now intent on damaging them to maximum effect. They were drinking beer in the shower. Some even did so in the toilets.

Chris showered quietly, enjoying the silly antics of the others. He washed his hair as best he could, trying to prevent water and soap getting into his wound. Now that the adrenalin was starting to decline he was beginning to feel the pain in his head.

The next morning the team was still celebrating. Most had not gone to bed. Chris had had a good night, electing to drink beer rather than take painkillers. He awoke at 10.30am and his head was hurting for three reasons. He had an injury. He had drunk too much beer, but most of all he needed to see Sarah.

35. A new start

Chris had not realised that the next few weeks would be very busy. He appeared on several television programmes. Articles about him had been in all the major newspapers and rugby league was in the unusual position of being in the national eye for nearly two weeks. As the match winner and obvious hero, Chris was the centre of attention and questions were always asked about Karl. Chris was always sensitive because Sarah and her family might be watching and always said the same thing. He was grateful for the inspiration that Karl had given him and said that he wouldn't have achieved what he had if it hadn't been for Karl.

One interview almost floored him when he was asked about his imminent transfer to Wigan. Chris denied any such transfer was taking place, but rumours persisted as sports writers desperate for a story matched the sport's spin doctors anxious to prolong the exposure. Chris continued with his denials, but the stories were beginning to become a nuisance that wouldn't go away.

In response to one persistent reporter who had telephoned him several times for a comment Chris said "I'm considering my future very carefully. I've not finalised my plans. Nothing has been decided."

He had hoped that this would have stopped any further enquiries, but it only served to fuel the rumour mill. He could not seem to shut them up. He needed to act quickly.

Three weeks after the final Chris sat in his car listening to the radio as the last of the morning's commuters disappeared into their workplaces. He followed the directions out of the city. He passed the university sports grounds that seemed to stretch for miles. In the distance, the cricket field disappeared into a row of oak and sycamore trees. As he had been told that the school was next to the university grounds, he presumed that these trees formed the boundary between the two institutions. He began to slow as he neared the trees and then saw the sign, half hidden among overgrown bushes, indicating that he had found the school.

He turned his car through the entrance and entered a long drive surrounded by tall hedgerows on either side. The drive was uneven and potholed and he nursed his car along the half mud, half gravel track that swept leftwards and then rightwards before depositing him in a car park marked 'Visitors only'.

The school seemed to be a hotchpotch of different single-storey buildings cobbled together by a drunken architect. One of the first things that struck him was the number of ramps outside each building. In fact, there were no steps at all. This was a place where steps were not useful. As he walked up the slow ramp to the entrance a wheelchair with a tiny frame inside it whizzed past from left to right. Chris stared at the wide glass front that had the word 'Entrance', in blue letters fixed to a wooden framed wall at the side. He pressed the bell and a voice answered: "Yes?"

Chris bent down to where the microphone appeared to be and said, "It's Chris Anderton. I've come to see the headmaster."

"Push the door please."

As he reached for the handle the intercom switched off, but not before he heard the woman say "It's Chris Anderton."

Chris smiled. As he entered the building he turned left into a light blue corridor and was immediately faced with several wheelchairs with one containing the same tiny frame he had seen earlier, hurtling towards him. As he jumped with fright the occupant steered the chair skilfully round him without slowing. Obviously excited and with a big grin on his face he half laughed, half gargled his way past. In a moment, before Chris had a chance to speak, the little boy had veered right through a large double door followed by five more children.

Immediately he heard a woman's voice shout, "David, slow down! How many times have I told you? You're going to kill someone!" For a second there was silence. Then the woman popped her head round the door. She was just in the middle of apologising when a second voice spoke from behind: "Mr Anderton?"

Chris turned and acknowledged the woman who had disappeared back into the classroom. He turned once more to face a man in a brown suit. In his late 40s he had an engaging smile that flashed over the beginnings of a double chin.

"Hello. I'm Mike Coates, the head teacher. We spoke on the phone last week."

"Yes." They shook hands warmly.

Coates took his guest into his office which sat in a little alcove just off the blue corridor, next to the reception desk.

"Would you like a cup of tea, coffee?"

As Chris sat drinking his cup of black tea he asked question after question. He found out that the school served a wide area; it took kids who were severely, physically disabled who required a level of attention not provided in mainstream schools. He found that there was an attempt underway to integrate these children into schools as much as possible, but that the stumbling block was always money and that perhaps there were some kids who were probably never going to fit into a mainstream school.

"Does that mean that they will always be kept separate?"

"I'm saying," replied Coates "that while schools are about nothing other than passing tests and exams and doing well in league tables then many of our kids reduce the performance of schools because they can't achieve as well or as quickly as others."

"So they drag a school down?"

"That's not a phrase I would care to use, but others might. I mean I'd argue that the kids you see here can be a positive benefit to schools if only they were given a chance. You said you'd been to Helen Keller College?"

Chris nodded. "Earlier this year."

"Well they will tell you that they have had some outstanding successes. For example Andrew was a lad with cerebral palsy. That's a condition caused by a lack of oxygen at birth. He can't walk. He has to have help feeding and toileting himself and yet he has just been accepted for a university course in computing."

"That's amazing."

"There are a lot of amazing people here Mr Anderton."

"Call me Chris."

"There are a lot of amazing people here." He paused "And I include the staff." There was another pause as the Head stared out of his window at a member of staff who was escorting a pupil across a covered walkway.

"We do a fantastic job." He turned to Chris "A fantastic job."

Chris smiled and nodded, struck by his obvious sincerity and pride in his school. There was another silence as Coates stood there watching, hands behind his back

"Would you like to see the place?"

"Yes please, Mr Coates."

"Do call me Mike."

The two men left his office and walked into the blue corridor which had a slight slope on it.

"What's it like teaching them? I suppose it's very demanding?"

"Yes, but it can be very rewarding. Can be a right bugger as well, especially when someone dies."

"Does that happen often?"

"It happens enough. It's impossible not to get involved. You get to know them so well. It's a nice job. It is, but it can be a right bugger. We deal with children of all kinds of issues, not just muscular dystrophy. As I said, we have many people who lead very successful lives, but muscular dystrophy, that's tough on everyone it touches."

"I know."

"Don't get me wrong. Some of those lads are brilliant people, absolutely brilliant."

They walked in silence past the glass entrance that gave the visitor an immediate impression of lightness and airiness. Chris was struck by the positive way the head teacher talked about his children and staff.

He was introduced to Miss Netherton, the figure who had popped out before when David had nearly cut him in two. David sat there along with the other pupils, grinning.

196

"Good morning everyone." said Mike "We have a visitor. He plays for Castleton." With that they all grinned and smiled. "Ah they all know who you are!"

Chris smiled back.

"And Great Britain!"

"Did you watch it?"

"Oh aye. Me dad went."

The young boy's hand moved slowly towards Chris's and he found himself shaking everyone's hand in turn.

It was all done in slow motion. He was touched by their weakness and at the same time, their strength. He had not planned the visit to be that of a celebrity, but he could not avoid young hands everywhere wanting to touch him and shake his hand.

The two men left the room and returned to the blue corridor. Turning left Chris asked, "Do they always smile so much?"

Mike laughed. "No they don't! Some of them can get real strops on. I can tell you. They are no different to you or me except they are often frustrated and sometimes angry."

"About?"

"Life. Why them? Why not you? That sort of thing. Why can you run around and they can't?"

"So they are angry?"

"Some are. Some aren't. They are no different to you and me. Some of them are bitter, some are absolute saints and some just do their best."

They turned left into a yellow corridor. The place was bright and cheeriness oozed out of every corner. They passed dozens of paintings and pictures mounted on the walls.

"These were done by our students."

"You're joking!" Chris could not hide his genuine surprise.

"No. David is studying photography at college."

"Why is he here?"

"He comes back twice a week for physiotherapy and a social. That's very important. Some of them have no friends apart from here."

They had arrived at the physiotherapy unit.

"What kind of therapy do you do?"

"Anything and everything. It's all dictated by the students' needs."

As they approached an electric motor whirred and the double doors opened.

Chris had never seen anything like it before. Two children were stood up, but were strapped to some form of stretcher. Chris did not ask in front of the children, but it seemed that they were being stretched.

"It helps stretch and strengthen the spine." Mike explained. Chris just nodded as if he had known but he hadn't. He was simply amazed.

A third boy lay on a bed and was being strapped in ready to be stood up against the wall. This was a hive of activity. All kinds of staff were moving to and fro seeing to the needs of different students. From the corner of the room he could hear shouts.

"Let's have a look at the pool." Mike almost pushed Chris in his enthusiasm to show him what they did for the kids. Putting on blue, sterile bags over the shoes they entered into the pool area. It was a small pool, not much bigger than a film star's private house pool, but in it, a young girl was approaching the side. Facing her at the pool side was a member of staff in a yellow plastic apron. She was holding out her hand encouraging, almost bullying, pleading with her to reach the side. When she touched her goal a woman in the pool who had been alongside her lifted her into the hands of the woman in the apron who gave out a shout of victory and applauded her young heroine. The woman in the yellow apron wrapped a towel round her as the girl grinned from ear to ear. The woman in yellow hugged her as if she had won a gold medal. Chris found himself smiling. He was pleased for the girl and admired the staff, none of whom he had ever met. This was a place where people make a real difference, he thought to himself. He was in awe of them, struck by the effort and dedication.

After half an hour Chris was back at the main entrance. He turned to his host and they shook hands.

"Thank you. It's been an eye opener."

"Anytime. Perhaps you could bring some of your colleagues some time? The kids would really love that."

"I'll sort something out before I leave."

"Leave? So are you going to Wigan?"

Chris half smiled and half cringed that he'd let anything slip.

"I don't know what's going to happen yet, but being here reminds you of what real life is like." He stopped and thought for a moment.

"Let's just say that I have a job to do."

Mike smiled knowingly without having the faintest idea of what he was on about.

"Well good luck then. I'll be sorry to see you go."

Chris smiled as the lights of his car flashed in response to his signal. He had only been at the school for an hour, but it would turn out to be an hour that would change his life.

36. The future

One month after the Final, Sarah took a job working on the checkout at a local supermarket. She had recovered from her bout of depression following Karl's death. If she had been asked, she would have replied that she was feeling much better. She had put on weight and was taking life as it came, one day at a time.

She found the nights difficult. There was very little to do, or at least very little compared to the demands of her previous life.

Sarah took delight in the simple things of life and valued the time that her children spent at home. Increasingly, however, they were spending more time with friends. She had encouraged it. She wanted them to live as normal a life as possible, but it left her alone a lot of the time. Often, she found herself looking out of the front window watching the world go by. Sometimes she stood there for a half an hour or more. Then she would chastise herself for being stupid and tell herself to get a life. Dealing with her new 'freedom' was proving to be difficult, however. Before she had often felt alone, now she was alone.

She would watch something boring on television or flick through a magazine occasionally. Sarah used to enjoy reading, but she couldn't seem to concentrate for long. Sometimes she found herself staring at the telephone hoping it would ring but a watched phone never rings.

She had rung him three times, but each time she had put the receiver down without leaving a message. She was frightened he would reject her. After all, she had refused to speak to him on several occasions, according to her mother at least. She had no recollection of it. She sat there alone. It was four o'clock and a week before Christmas. She picked up the phone.

"To hell with it Christopher Anderton. If you don't want to, you don't want to." She rang the number and this time, to her surprise, someone answered. The voice at the other end belonged to a woman.

One month after the final at the same time as Sarah was phoning him at home, Chris Anderton passed through the main entrance of the church once more. A cold gentle wind kept giving hints of snowfall. He turned to close the pedestrian gate. He liked the sound of wooden gates banging into their frames. Checking that it was shut and that it wouldn't bang in the wind he turned to walk past the church and down to the graveyard.

Chris felt most comfortable in casual clothes and trainers. His normal outdoor clothing would normally be a waterproof walking jacket. Today, however, was special. He had come to pay his respects and had prepared accordingly. Dressed in a light grey suit with a white shirt and blue tie he felt clean and comfortable. This was unusual. He had never enjoyed suits. Perhaps it was because his size always made it difficult to get comfortable with shirts and ties. Today was different. For the first time in his life he had bought a suit that was made to measure and the tailor had taken great care to dress him well. He was even wearing scent. He was going to do this properly. Over his suit he wore a full-length woollen blue overcoat. He looked and felt good.

As he passed the church entrance, he stood to admire the arched double doors. They were old with large black hinges. At their centre were two circular, wrought iron knockers come handles. He liked old buildings, especially churches. They were comfortable. For a moment as he stood there, his breath disappearing in the damp air, he looked almost distinguished.

He sighed as he slowly turned towards the graveyard. He had a job to do and he wanted to be ready. Walking slowly, he fiddled with the flowers that he carried. He was nervous.

The cinder path crunched beneath his feet. He realised that he had not noticed much about the graveyard on his previous visit. He had had other things on his mind. As he passed through the gap in the hedge that took him into the graveyard it was bigger than he remembered. He realised to his chagrin that he couldn't quite remember where the grave was.

The path ended and he stepped onto the grass, heading in the rough direction that he thought he remembered. He stood at the end of the seventh row, looking for newly turned earth. There were three. The gravediggers had been busy. None of them were Karl's. Turning round he looked anxiously, then in the fading light he saw it. He saw the gravestone that he had paid for. Sarah could not afford a proper stone and he had asked her permission to buy one at the funeral. At first she refused, but when he told her what he thought should go on it she had relented.

Now he could see it. Nervously he moved towards the marble headstone that stood at the head of the grave. It was whiter than the thickening snow that was now carpeting the ground. On its top stood a small replica of the world cup in gold leaf. Around the cup's base fluttered ribbons coloured red, white and blue.

The gold letters read "Karl James Burgess. Aged 17. Braver Than All The Rest." He was pleased. It was fitting. It had style. He laid the flowers reverently beneath the stone and stood at the foot of the grave. His chest heaved. Chris checked that he was alone and again his chest heaved.

"I thought I'd come and pay a visit. I wanted to check that it was okay and it is. They've done you proud." He shuffled awkwardly. He put his hands behind his back and then dropped them to his side. Before he spoke he held them together almost prayer like. Then they dropped to his side once more. He wished he'd kept hold of the flowers. They would have given his hands something to do.

He cleared his throat and was conscious that his eyes were filling. Coughing, he fought back the tears. He wasn't ashamed to cry, but he had something to say. It was important. He had prepared this moment thoroughly and he wanted it to sound as he intended. Although he was sad there could be no place for tears.

"Thank you" he blurted. He coughed once more. He was annoyed with himself. He wanted to be clear. He pulled a handkerchief from his pocket and blew into it. Once more his chest heaved. Chris took his time. He swallowed. "I wanted to tell you that I know what you did for me." His head bowed for a second. Once more he looked at the stone.

"I know what you did."

He paused and looked knowingly at the stone. "All the time I thought I was helping you and you were helping me."

"Thanks".

"I've been rehearsing this" he whispered. "I wanted to make sure you knew. Now, thanks seems so quick. But it's what I wanted to say."

As he spoke these last words his voice crumbled to a whisper and died. The tears rolled down his face as he bit his lip. He half turned for a moment as if to run away but he stopped himself and looked at the stone once more. The big man wept and then stopped himself. He pulled the handkerchief from his pocket once more. He wiped his eyes and then stood, holding the hankie in his hands. He'd found something to do with his hands. It seemed to relax him. Gathering himself together he stared at the grave, at the silence.

"You never stood a chance did you? And I don't think I ever heard you complain." He sniffed. "Er. You never complained. You just got on with it. I know you didn't have a choice and that words like bravery can mean nothing but you had a choice in how you dealt with it and you showed me something. I realise that I wouldn't have done what I did if it hadn't been for you and I just wanted to say thanks."

"I know where I'm going now. You showed me what I must do and it's amazing really. I never thought it would be this. When you are a performer, you are very self-centred. You have to be really. You constantly think about yourself, how you are doing, how much you can get for it, but I don't want that anymore. I want to do something useful, no more games. No, no more games."

He stood there thinking, looking for the next line. "Something useful," and with those simple words he stopped crying. He even stopped being upset. In fact, he started smiling. Suddenly his sadness disappeared as self-realisation came over him.

"I know where I'm going. Thanks".

He put his hand into his right pocket and took out a small jewellery box, its top inscribed with the initials of the International Rugby League Federation.

He opened it and took out his World Cup Winners medal.

"I thought you ought to have this. You earned it."

He bent down and pushed it deep into the soil at the foot of the stone so that it could not be seen.

He stood there in silence wiping the soil and snow from his fingers.

"There's one other thing. I'd like to see your mum again. I don't know if she wants to see me. It's up to her. It's too soon perhaps but... Anyway, I thought I'd let you know."

Finally, after some time he began to feel the cold biting through his coat. It was getting colder. It was time to go.

"Bye," and with those brief words he turned to leave.

"Hello Chris" her voice whispered.

He turned and gasped as he saw a ghost like figure. She was dressed in a long grey coat and stood with the light behind her.

"Bloody hell!"

"I'm sorry." There was a pause as Chris recovered from his shock.

"I thought you were a ghost."

She smiled. "Your sister told me that you would be here. I didn't know you had a sister. You never mentioned her."

"I never thought to. There was always something more important."

Another pause showered them in snow.

"You did well."

"Thanks. I saw you, but you left."

"I had to. It was awkward pushing that heavy wheelchair and I was freezing cold."

"Ah."

"I phoned you several times."

"I believe so. I was ill."

He nodded quietly. He took a step towards her and she did likewise. Their hands touched gently, lightly and then they embraced.

"I love you. I've missed you."

"I love you too. I had no strength. I couldn't deal with it."

"I know. Sssh. Don't fret. It's going to be okay."

They stood there, getting whiter, in each others' arms impervious to the cold.

"I wanted to talk to you. I did."

He soothed her anxious words and stroked her head gently. "You've been through so much."

He buried her head in his chest so that she couldn't make any more unnecessary apologies. "It's time to go."

She nodded and they turned towards the church and home.

As they left the graveyard and began the slow climb into the church grounds she stopped once more.

"Thanks."

"What for?"

"You waited for me."

He took hold of her hand and kissed it. "I'd have waited for ever."

Behind them lay the disturbed and twisted surface of the snow. Ahead lay a white canvas, clean and unblemished. They turned and walked together to meet it.

All night the snow fell. The graves lay tucked in under the warm blanket. By morning all trace of their footsteps had gone.

Next evening the 6.20pm sports news followed the national and local news on the radio as it always did. There was a story about the forthcoming England football match against Brazil.

In her kitchen Sarah finished wiping the dishes from tea time. The kids were in the front room. She finished the dishes as she half listened to the radio. She put the last items of cutlery into the drawer then she returned to the sink to rinse out the bowl. As she did so she stopped when the sports commentator said "And now to rugby league. The Castleton rugby league club have announced today that they are to part company with their club captain, Chris Anderton, who has announced his retirement with immediate effect. George Sotherby, the club's chief executive, said that although the departure was sudden and unexpected, they fully appreciated Anderton's reasons for doing so which were personal. He added that while the club was sorry to see him go they wished him well in his new venture. It is believed he is to go to college to begin training to teach children with special needs."

Sarah smiled. Chris had told her of his plans the previous night. For the first time that she could remember she was genuinely happy. Life was going to be normal from now on. She could see a future.

She was looking forward to it.

Appendix: Rugby League

Rugby League began its life in 1895 as a breakaway from the sport of Rugby Union. It was originally called Northern Union. As the game had developed during the second half of the nineteenth century, particularly in the industrial northern areas, cup competitions and leagues started in the 1870s and 1880s. Its popularity grew and the clubs became more commercial, developing grounds and charging admission fees for matches.

It placed more and more demands on players' time. The game's headquarters were based in the south of England. Its leadership, committed to a philosophy of pure amateurism, could and would not appreciate the fact that working class men in the industrial north had real problems when trying to play sport. They often lost wages due to time off work to travel to and play in matches, and an injury could bring about considerable financial hardship.

Rugby Union's refusal to allow payment for 'broken time' – compensation for lost wages – saw a crisis develop which led to suspensions of players and clubs for alleged breaches of the rules on 'amateurism' and a split in the game resulting in two versions of rugby. Union was mainly a middle and upper class game based mainly, but not entirely, in the south of England while the Northern Union was played predominantly by the working class men in the north. The leadership of the rugby union had seen how the development of professionalism in association football had seen that sport become dominated by professional clubs in the industrial areas, and were determined that the same would not happen in rugby union.

Within a couple of years, part-time professionalism was accepted in the Northern Union. Several rule changes followed to make the game more attractive to watch for spectators. This included reducing the number of players to 13-a-side, changing the tackle rule and the points scoring system.

In 1922 the Northern Union became The Rugby Football League. A different game had developed with a separate culture and heritage. From the split in 1895, anyone playing for a Northern Union club was banned from playing rugby union again. This ban was lifted after 1995, when rugby union finally accepted professionalism. Now players can play both sports without problems from officialdom.

I am proud of this heritage. Rugby League has a proud history of community spirit and inclusiveness. It has had two black captains of its national team in Clive Sullivan and Ellery Hanley. Indeed Sullivan was the first black captain of any British national side.

It has developed a strong philosophy of sport for all. In 1980, Fulham RLFC established a professional rugby league club in London for the first time since the 1930s. The Rugby League Conference, played in the summer with amateur players, has seen the sport develop on a national basis. The Rugby Football League has promoted women's and girls' rugby and has a national wheelchair rugby league side. Recently a disabled former player who is confined to a wheelchair obtained a coaching certificate.

Top rugby league players earn much less than football players yet they are just as fit and skilful and stronger. It is a disgrace that a sport that is now played in every county in England and Wales is so often ignored by the union biased media.

As with any sport, although the top of the game is professional, the vast majority of players are amateurs, playing for enjoyment. In the professional game in Europe, the top competition is the Super League, which includes clubs from London, Wales and Frances as well as Lancashire and Yorkshire. The Challenge Cup has been played for since 1897, with the final held at Wembley.

Internationally, the sport has also developed a far wider base than in the past. England, Australia and New Zealand are still its strongest base. The game has a tradition in France dating back to the 1930s, despite being banned by the Vichy regime during the Second World War. There are leagues and national teams representing Ireland, Wales and Scotland. In Papua New Guinea it is the national sport, and is very popular in the South Sea Islands, including Samoa, Tonga and Fiji. More European countries, including Russia, now play the game, and it has also established roots in South Africa, Morocco, Lebanon, the USA and Jamaica.

It is a sport which has been discriminated against throughout its entire existence yet it remains successful and resilient. I am proud to be a supporter of this sport and hope that in some small way this book helps to promote it to a wider audience.

Teams in rugby league have 13 players on each side. Matches last two halves of 40 minutes, a total of 80 minutes. Points are scored through tries and goals. A try, when the ball is touched down in the opposing team's goal area, are worth 4 points. This also gives the scoring team the chance to convert the try – kick a goal – worth another two points for successfully kicking it between the posts and over the cross bar of the H shaped goal. A penalty goal is also worth two points, and a drop goal, when the ball is kicked through the posts in open play on the half-volley is worth one point. Teams have five backs, two half backs and six forwards. The ball is passed backwards from one player to another. When a player is tackled – held on the ground by an opponent – the player in possession back heels the ball to a team mate standing behind him. This is known as 'play the ball'. Each team has six 'tackles' and on the sixth the ball turn over to the other team. Therefore teams often kick the ball downfield for distance or to set up a scoring chance on the 'sixth' tackle, rather than lose the ball. Tackling is not allowed above shoulder height.

Substitutions are allowed for tactical reasons, or if a player is injured, and, unlike in some other football codes, players can return as a substitute after coming off. In the professional game there are four substitutes, and up to 12 substitutions during a match.

In the professional game, the timekeeping is done independently from the referee. A hooter is sounded to start and finish each half, the end of the match is known as 'the final hooter'.

In all forms of the game, strict discipline applies. Players can be sent off for 10 minutes for offences ('sin-binned') and sent off for the rest of the match for serious foul play. Despite the tough physical nature of the sport, there is a tradition of respect for referees, partly because disputing a referee's decision can result in a penalty being moved 10 metres towards the player's own line, making it more likely that a goal can be kicked from it, or territory gained.

The pitch is a similar size to an association football pitch, 100 metres by 68 metres. At each end is the in goal area, six metres long, where tries are scored.

For more information, visit www.therfl.uk.com

Rugby league action from England Students versus Australia Students in 2007 at the New River Stadium in London.
Top: A tackle in open play
Middle: A scrum.
Bottom: Open play showing the posts.
(Photos: Peter Lush)

Best in the Northern Union

The pioneering 1910 Rugby League Lions tour of Australia and New Zealand

Tom Mather

Tom Mather's fascinating account of the first tour 'down under ' by the British Rugby League Lions, which helped establish the sport in Australia and New Zealand, and gave rugby league an international dimension. Published in 2010 at £12.95. Available direct from London League Publications Ltd for just £12.00 post free. For credit card payments visit www.llpshop.co.uk , cheque payments to PO Box 10441, London E14 8WR, payable to London League publications Ltd. It can also be ordered from any bookshop for £12.95 (ISBN: 9781903659519).

Hunslet through and through
Geoff Gunney MBE, rugby league footballer

Maurice Bamford

Geoff Gunney was one of the great players of post-war rugby league and a stalwart of the Hunslet club. Former Great Britain coach Maurice Bamford outlines his career in an authorised biography published in 2010. Published at £13.95. Available direct from London League Publications Ltd for just £13.00. For credit card payments visit www.llpshop.co.uk , cheque payments to PO Box 10441, London E14 8WR, cheques payable to London League publications Ltd. It can also be ordered from any bookshop for £13.95 (ISBN: 9781903659465).

New books from London League Publications Ltd

No sand dunes in Featherstone
Memories of West Yorkshire Rugby League
Edited by Robert Light

Based on the 'Up and Under' University of Huddersfield oral history project, this book includes memories from players, coaches, club officials, referees, journalists and supporters from the First World War to the present. Every rugby league supporter will enjoy this fascinating book.

To be published in October 2010 at £12.95. Available direct from London League Publications Ltd for just £12.00. For credit card payments visit www.llpshop.co.uk , cheque payments to PO Box 10441, London E14 8WR, cheques payable to London League publications Ltd. It can also be ordered from any bookshop for £12.95 (ISBN: 9781903659533).

Calm in the Cauldron
A rugby league journey
John Dorahy
with Tom Mather

John Dorahy was a great player in Australia in the 1970s and 1980s. He was also a successful coach. This autobiography covers his full career, including his time in England with Hull KR, Halifax, Wigan and Warrington.
To be published in November 2010 at £13.95. Available direct from London League Publications Ltd for just £13.00. For credit card payments visit www.llpshop.co.uk , cheque payments to PO Box 10441, London E14 8WR, cheques payable to London League publications Ltd. It can also be ordered from any bookshop for £13.95 (ISBN: 9781903659540).